BEYOND LIFE

BOOKS BY MR. CABELL

Essays:

BEYOND LIFE

Novels:

THE CREAM OF THE JEST
THE SOUL OF MELICENT
THE RIVET IN GRANDFATHER'S NECK
THE CORDS OF VANITY
THE EAGLE'S SHADOW

Tales:

THE CERTAIN HOUR
CHIVALRY
THE LINE OF LOVE
GALLANTRY

Verses:

FROM THE HIDDEN WAY

Genealogies:

BRANCH OF ABINGDON
BRANCHIANA
THE MAJORS AND THEIR MARRIAGES

BEYOND
LIFE

Dizain des Démiurges

BY

JAMES BRANCH CABELL

"Many a man lives a burden to the earth: but a good book is the precious life-blood of a master-spirit, embalmed and treasured up on purpose to a life beyond life."

NEW YORK
ROBERT M. MCBRIDE & COMPANY
1919

Printed in the United States of America.

Second Printing, March, 1919.

Published January, 1919.

To

GUY HOLT

Garrulity again begets
Unconscionable dreadful debts. . .

You that have piped to-day must dance;
Herein beholding maintenance
Of arguments about Romance
(Like fountains falling whence they spring)
To you revert its eddying.

Contents

I

WE APPROACH

—So I propose to settle the matter, once for all. In fact I feel myself in rather good form and about to shine to perhaps exceptional advantage. . .

—Hark to the fellow! . . But riddle me this, now, in the name of Œdipus! who wants to hear about your moonstruck theories?

—Such, Curly-Locks, is not the game I quest. . . I propose to lecture to bare benches; granted Indeed, it would be base to deceive you. But is it not apparent —even, as one might say uncivilly, to you—that the lack of an audience breeds edifying candor in the speaker? and leads him presently to overhear a discovery of his actual opinion?

—*Ashtaroth's Lackey*

I

Wherein We Approach All Authors at Their Best.

WHENEVER I am in Fairhaven, if but in thought, I desire the company of John Charteris. His morals I am not called upon to defend, nor do I esteem myself really responsible therefor: and from his notions I frequently get entertainment . . .

Besides, to visit Charteris realizes for you the art of retaining "an atmosphere," because Willoughby Hall, to the last mullion and gable, is so precisely the mansion which one would accredit in imagination to the author of *In Old Lichfield,* and *Ashtaroth's Lackey,* and all those other stories of the gracious Southern life of more stately years. . . But pictures of this eighteenth century manor-house have been so often reproduced in literary supplements and magazines that to describe Willoughby Hall appears superfluous.

Fairhaven itself, I find, has in the matter of "atmosphere" deteriorated rather appallingly since the town's northern outskirt was disfigured by a powder mill. Unfamiliar persons, in new-looking clothes, now walk on Cambridge Street, with an unseemly effect of actual haste to reach their destination; and thus pass unabashed by St. Martin's Churchyard, wherein they have not any great-grandparents. Immediately across the street from the churchyard now glitters the Colonial Moving Picture Palace: and most of the delectable old-fashioned aborigines "take boarders" (at unbelievable rates), and time-honored King's College rents out its dormitories in summer months to the munition workers. Then, too, everybody has money. . . In fine, there remains for the future historian who would perfectly indicate how incredible were the changes wrought by recent years, merely to make the statement that Fairhaven was synchronized. For without any intermediary gradations the town has passed from the eighteenth to the twentieth century.

2

But Willoughby Hall had remained unchanged since my last visit, save for the installation of electric lights. Charteris I think it must have been who attended to it that these were so discreetly placed and shaded that nowhere do you actually see an anachronistic bulb; for the wizened little fellow attaches far more importance to such details than does his wife: and on each of his mantles you may still find a sheaf of paper "lamp-lighters." He probably rolls them himself, in his determined retention of "atmosphere."

His library and working-room, at all events, is a personal apartment such as does not seem likely ever to be much affected by extraneous happenings. His library opens upon a sort of garden, which is mostly lawn and trees: this side of the room I can only describe as made of glass; for it is all one broad tall window, in three compartments, with a window-seat beneath. To-night the shutters were closed; but still you were conscious of green growing things very close at hand. . . The other walls are papered, as near as I remember, in a brown leather-like shade, obscurely patterned in dull gold: the bookcases ranged against them are flagrantly irregular in shape and height, and convey the impression of having been acquired one by one, as the increasing number of books in the library demanded augmented shelf-room. Above and between these cases are the originals of various paintings made to illustrate the writings of John Charteris: and the walls are furthermore adorned with numerous portraits of those whom Charteris described to me as his "literary creditors." . . This assemblage is sufficiently curious. . .

Here, then, we were sitting, toward nine o'clock on a pleasant evening in May, what time John Charteris apologized for having nothing in particular to talk about. I courteously suggested that the circumstance was never once aforetime known to keep him silent.

3

"Ah, but then you must remember," says Charteris, "that you find me a little let down by a rather trying day. I devoted an arduous morning to splashing about the room with a tin basin and a couple of old towels, washing off the glass in all my several million pictures. They really do get terribly dirty, what with their misguided owner's pertinacious efforts toward ruining his health by incessant smoking."

"But surely——! well, why on earth do you attend to that sort of thing?"

"For the simple reason, my dear fellow, that

we never had a housegirl who could wash pictures without slopping the water through at the corners, and making unpleasant looking brown spots. I practically exist in here: and I find it worth my while to have my lair just what I want it, even at the cost of doing my own housecleaning. Picture-washing, after all, is not so trying as polishing the furniture. I do not so much mind the smell, but at times it seems to me there is something vaguely ridiculous in the spectacle of a highly gifted novelist sitting upon the floor and devoting all his undeniable ability to getting the proper polish on a chair leg. Besides, I am not so limber as I used to be."

"At worst, though, Charteris, all this will be an interesting trait for the Authorized Biography,—when some unusually discreet person has been retained to edit and censor the story of your life—"

A bit forlornly he said: "Ah, yes, the story of my life! That reminds me I put in the afternoon typing off some letters I had from a girl, I very emphatically decline to say how many years ago. I want to use her in the new book, and from letters, somehow, one gets more of a genuine accent, of a real flavor, than it is easy

7

to invent. Indeed, as I grow older I find it impossible to 'do' a satisfactory heroine without a packet of old love-letters to start on—and to work in here and there, you know, for dialogue. . . Ah, but then, in that tin box just back of your chair, I have filed the letters of eight women which I have not used yet, and to-day I foolishly got to glancing over the whole budget. . . . And it was rather depressing. It made my life, on looking back, seem too much like a very loosely connected series of short stories. The thing was not sound art. It lacked construction, form, inevitability—perhaps I cannot quite word what I mean! But so many wonderful and generous women! and so much that once seemed so very important! and nothing to come of any of it! Oh, yes, old letters are infernal things.''

"But useful for literary purposes," I suggested, "if only one happens to be a particularly methodical and cold-blooded sort of ghoul.''

He shrugged. "Oh, yes, one has to be, in the interest of romantic art. I am afraid almost everything is grist for that omnivorous mill. It seemed to me, this afternoon at least, that even I was very like a character being carried

over from one short story to another, and then
to yet another. And I could not but suspect
that, so as to make me fit into my new surroundings more exactly, at every transfer I was
altered a bit, not always for the better. In fine,
there seems to be an Author who coarsens and
cheapens and will some day obliterate me, in
order to serve the trend of some big serial he
has in course of publication. For as set against
that, I am of minor importance. Indeed, it was
perhaps simply to further this purpose that he
created me. I wonder?"

"Your notion," I observed, with dignity,
"has been elsewhere handled——"

"But it has not been disposed of," retorted
Charteris, "and it will never down. The riddle
of the Author and his puppets, and of their
true relations, stays forever unanswered. And
no matter from what standpoint you look at it,
there seems an element of unfairness. . ."

"The Author works according to his
creed——"

"But we do not know what it is. We cannot
even guess. Ah, I dare say you wonder quite
as often as I do what the Author is up to."
And I regarded the little man with real tenderness: for I saw that he justified the far-fetched

9

analogue I had aforetime employed in speaking of John Charteris, when I likened him to a quizzical black parrot . . .

4

"Probably no author," I suggested, "can ever, quite, put his actual working creed into any hard and fast words that satisfy him."

"But no self-respecting author, my dear man, has ever pretended to put anything into words that satisfied him."

"Well, for one, I write my books as well as I can. I have my standards, undoubtedly, and I value them——"

"You tell us, in effect, that Queen Anne is dead."

"And I believe them to be the standards of every person that ever wrote a re-readable book. Yet I question if I could tell you precisely what these standards are."

"They are very strikingly exemplified, however"—and John Charteris waved his hand,—"on every side of us. But how can you hope to judge of books, who have never read any author in the only satisfactory edition?" . .

5

For we were sitting, I may repeat, in his

library at Willoughby Hall, where I had often been before. But I had never thought to examine his bookshelves, as I did now . . .

"Why, what on earth, Charteris——! The Complete Works of David Copperfield: Œuvres de Lucien de Rubempré: Novels and Tales of Mark Ambient: Novels of Titus Scrope: The Works of Arthur Pendennis: Complete Writings of Eustace Cleever: Works of Bartholomew Josselin: Poems of Gervase Poore: The Works of Colney Durance:"— hastily I ran over some of the titles. "Why, what on earth are all these library sets?"

"That section of the room is devoted to the books of the gifted writers of Bookland. You will observe it is extensive; for the wonderful literary genius is by long odds the most common character in fiction. You will find all my books over there, I may diffidently remark."

"H'm, yes," said I,—"no doubt!"

But I was inspecting severally Lord Bendish's *Billiad* and *The Wanderer;* and *A Man of Words,* by Felix Wildmay; and *The Amber Statuette,* by Lucien Taylor; and the *Collected Essays* of Ernest Pontifex; and in particular, an interesting publication entitled *The Nungapunga Book,* by G. B. Torpenhow, with Numer-

11

ous Illustrations by Richard Heldar . . . .

And I even looked provisionally into *An Essay upon Castametation, with some particular Remarks upon the Vestiges of Ancient Fortifications lately discovered by the Author at the Kaim of Kinprunes* . . .

6

Then I became aware of further food for wonder. "Why, but what's this—*Sophia Scarlet, The Shovels of Newton French, Cannonmills, The Rising Sun*—You seem to have a lot of Stevenson's I never heard of."

"Those shelves contain the cream of the unwritten books—the masterpieces that were planned and never carried through. Of them also, you perceive, there are a great many. Indeed, a number of persons who never published a line have contributed to that section. Yes, that is Thackeray's mediæval romance of Agincourt. Dickens, as you see, has several novels there: perhaps *The Young Person* and *The Children of the Fathers* are the best, but they all belong to his later and failing period——"

"But the unwritten books appear to run largely to verse——"

12

" 'For many men are poets in their youth', and in their second childhood also. That Keats' epic thing is rather disappointing: and, for one, I cannot agree with Hawthorne's friend that it contains 'the loftiest strains which have been heard on earth since Milton's day.' Milton's own *King Arthur*, by the by, is quite his most readable performance. And that?——oh, yes, the complete *Christabel* falls off toward the end and becomes fearfully long-winded. And the last six books of *The Faery Queen* and the latter *Canterbury Tales* are simply beyond human patience——"

"Then too there is a deal of drama. But what is Sheridan doing in this galley?"

"Why, that volume is an illustrated edition of Sheridan's fine comedy, *Affectation,* which he mulled over during the last thirty years of his life: and it is undisputedly his masterpiece. The main treasure of my library, though, is that unbound collection of the Unwritten Plays of Christopher Marlowe."

7

"This part of the room, at least"—for I was still nosing about—"appears to exhibit much the usual lot of standard books——"

"Ah, if those only were the ordinary standards for inducing sleep!"—and Charteris shrugged. "Instead, those are the books with which you are familiar, as the authors meant them to be."

"Then even Shakespeare came an occasional cropper——?"

"Oh, that is the 1599 version of *Troilus and Cressida*—the only edition in which the play is anything like comprehensible . . . You have no idea how differently books read in the Intended Edition. Why, even your own books," added Charteris, "in that Intended Edition yonder, issued through Knappe & Dreme—who bring out, indeed, the only desirable edition of most authors—are such as you might read with pleasure, and even a mild degree of pride."

"Go on!" said I, "for now I know you are talking nonsense."

"Upon my word," said he, "I really mean it." . .

8

Then, and then only, did I comprehend the singularity of that unequalled collection of literary masterpieces. . . "Man, man!" I said, in envy, "if I had shared your oppor-

14

tunities I would know well enough what a book ought to be. I might even be able to formulate the æsthetic creed of which I was just speaking.''

''I have heard, though,'' said Charteris, with a grin, ''that a quite definite sort of a something in this line has been accomplished. How was it Mr. Wilson Follett summed it up? Oh, yes!—'Reduced to baldness, the argument is this: Since first-class art has never reproduced its own contemporary background (for some reason or other the romanticist does not adduce Jane Austen in support of this truism), and since the novel of things-as-they-are calls for no constructive imagination whatever in author or reader, the present supply of ''realism'' is nothing but the publisher's answer to a cheap and fickle demand; and since the imaginative element in art is all but everything, the only artist who has a chance of longevity is he who shuns the ''vital'', the ''gripping'', and the contemporary.' Surely, that ought to be a creed quite definite enough for anybody accused of being committed to it.''

''Quite,'' I conceded—''especially since the charge is laid by a person whose dicta I am accustomed to revere and, elsewhere, to delight

15

in. Now to me that creed, as originally stated, read infinitely plainer than a pikestaff. Yet you see what an actually noteworthy critic like Mr. Follett makes of it: whereas, to the other side, one of the least frivolous of our comic weeklies, *The Independent,* described that very exposition of romantic ideals as 'fatuous'; and *The New York Times* was moved to mild deploring that the thing had not been suppressed. So I am afraid it was not put with entire exactness after all."

Charteris reflected. "At least," he said, in a while, "I would not have phrased it quite in Mr. Follett's manner, which reduces to baldness an argument that is entitled to hairsplitting. For nothing, even remotely, can compare with romance in importance. I am not speaking merely of that especial manifestation of romance which is sold in book-form. . . Well, as you may recall, I have been termed the founder of the Economist school of literature. I accept the distinction for what it is worth, and probably for a deal more. And I believe the Economist creed as to the laws of that 'life beyond life' which Milton attributes to good books could be explicitly stated in a few minutes. Of course, it

16

does require a little reading-up, in some library not less well stocked than mine with the really satisfactory editions."

"Then do you state it," I exhorted, "and save me the trouble of puzzling over it any longer." . . It was then a trifle after nine in the evening. . .

"Off-hand," began John Charteris, "I would say that books are best insured against oblivion through practise of the auctorial virtues of distinction and clarity, of beauty and symmetry, of tenderness and truth and urbanity. . ."

9

But—as you may hereinafter observe if such be your will—he did not explain his theories "in a few minutes." In fact, the little man talked for a long while, even until dawn; and as it appeared to me, not always quite consistently. And he seemed to take an impish delight in his own discursiveness, as he ran on, in that wonderfully pleasing voice of his: and he shifted from irony to earnestness, and back again, so irresponsibly that I was not always sure of his actual belief.

Thus it was that John Charteris discoursed,

as he sat there, just beyond the broad and gleaming expanse of desk-top, talking, interminably talking. The hook-nosed little fellow looks, nowadays, incredibly withered and ancient: one might liken him to a Pharaoh newly unwrapped were it not for his very unregal restlessness. And his eyes, too, stay young and a trifle puzzled. . . So Charteris talked: and animatedly he twisted in his swivel-chair, now toward me, now toward the unabridged dictionary mounted on a stand at his right elbow, and now toward the ashtray at his left. For of course he smoked I do not pretend to estimate how many cigarettes . . . Meanwhile he talked: and he talked in very much that redundant and finicky and involved and inverted "style" of his writings; wherein, as you have probably noted, the infrequent sentence which does not begin with a connective or with an adverb comes as a positive shock. . .

And sometimes he talked concerning men who have made literature, and spoke sensibly enough, although with a pervasive air of knowing more than anyone else ever did. And sometimes he discoursed enigmas, concerning the power of romance, which he pretentiously called "the demiurge", as being a world-shaping and world-controlling principle: and this appeared a plausible tenet when advanced by Charteris, if only because he declared himself to be a character out of romantic fiction; but I have since been tempted to question the theory's quite general application. And he talked a deal, too, concerning the "dynamic illusions" evolved by romance, which phrase I still consider unhappy, for all that deliberation suggests no synonym. . .

10

His notion, as I followed him, was that romance controlled the minds of men; and by creating force-producing illusions, furthered the world's betterment with the forces thus brought into being: so that each generation of naturally inert mortals was propelled toward a higher sphere and manner of living, by the might of each generation's ignorance and prejudices and follies and stupidities, beneficently directed. To me this sounded in every way Economical. And as he ran on, I really seemed to glimpse, under the spell of that melodious voice, romance and "realism" as the contending Ormuzd and Ahrimanes he depicted; and the ends for which these two contended as not merely scriptorial. . .

But I too run on. It is more equitable to let John Charteris speak for himself, and express uninterruptedly the creed of what he called the Economist theory, as to literature and human affairs in general. . .

II

THE DEMIURGE

—What is man, that his welfare be considered?—an ape who chatters to himself of kinship with the archangels while filthily he digs for groundnuts. . . .

—Yet more clearly do I perceive that this same man is a maimed god. . . . He is under penalty condemned to compute eternity with false weights and to estimate infinity with a yardstick; and he very often does it. . . .

—There lies the choice which every man must make— or rationally to accept his own limitations? or stupendously to play the fool and swear that he is at will omnipotent?

—Dizain des Reines

II

Which Deals with the Demiurge

OFF-HAND (began John Charteris) I would say that books are best insured against oblivion through practise of the auctorial virtues of distinction and clarity, of beauty and symmetry, of tenderness and truth and urbanity. That covers the ground, I think: and so it remains merely to cite supporting instances here and there, by mentioning a few writers who have observed these requirements, and thus to substantiate my formula without unnecessary divigation. . .

Therefore I shall be very brief. And even so, I imagine, you will not be inclined to listen to much of what I am about to say, if only because, like most of us, you are intimidated by that general attitude toward culture and the humanities which has made of American literature, among foreign penmen, if not precisely an object of despairing envy, at least of feeling comment. In particular, I imagine that my frequent references to the affairs and people of fled years will annoy you, since the American book-purchaser shies from such pedantic, and indeed from any, allusion to the past, with that distrust peculiar to persons with criminal records. In fact, this murderer, too, is often haunted, I dare say, by memories of his victim, in thinking of the time he has killed, whether with the "uplifting" or with the "daring" current novels of yesterday.

But you perceive, I trust, that your personal indifference, and the lazy contempt of America as a whole, toward art matters no more affects the eternal verity and the eternal importance of art than do the religious practises of Abyssinia, say, affect the verity and importance of the New Testament. You perceive, I trust, that you ought to be interested in art matters, whatever is your actual emotion. You understand, in fine—as a mere abstract principle—what your feeling "ought to be." Well, it is precisely that tendency to imagine yourself and your emotions as these things "ought to be" which convicts you, over any verbal disclaimer, of a vital interest in art matters: and it is that tendency about which I propose to speak very briefly. . .

And yet, so insidious is the influence of

general opinion, even when manifested as plain unreason, that I confess I myself, whenever anyone talks of "art" and "æsthetic theories", am inclined to find him vaguely ridiculous, and seem to detect in every word he utters a flavor of affectation. So should you prove quite as susceptible as I to the herd-instinct I shall have no ground for complaint. Meanwhile in theory—without of necessity accompanying my friend Felix Kennaston all the way to his conclusion that the sum of corporeal life represents an essay in romantic fiction,—I can perceive plainly enough that the shape-giving principle of all sentient beings is artistic. That is a mere matter of looking at living creatures and noticing their forms. . . But the principle goes deeper, in that it shapes too the minds of men, by this universal tendency to imagine—and to think of as in reality existent —all the tenants of earth and all the affairs of earth, not as they are, but "as they ought to be". And so it comes about that romance has invariably been the demiurgic and beneficent force, not merely in letters, but in every matter which concerns mankind; and that "realism", with its teaching that the mile-posts along the road are as worthy of consideration as the goal, has always figured as man's chief enemy. . .

2

Indeed, that scathing criticism which Sophocles passed, however anciently on a contemporary, remains no less familiar than significant,—"He paints men as they are: I paint them as they ought to be." It is aside from the mark that in imputing such veracity to Euripides the singer of Colonos was talking nonsense: the point is that Sophocles saw clearly what was the one unpardonable sin against art and human welfare.

For the Greeks, who were nurtured among art's masterworks, recognized, with much of that perturbing candor wherewith children everywhere appraise their associates, that gracefully to prevaricate about mankind and human existence was art's signal function. As a by-product of this perception, Hellenic literature restrained its endeavors, quite naturally, to embroidering events that were incontestable because time had erased the evidence for or against their actual occurrence: and poets evoked protagonists worth noble handling from bright mists of antiquity, wherethrough, as far

as went existent proofs, men might in reality
have moved "as they ought to be". Thus, even
Homer, the most ancient of great verbal artists,
elected to deal with legends that in his day were
venerable: and in Homer when Ajax lifts a
stone it is with the strength of ten warriors,
and Odysseus, when it at all promotes the
progress of the story, becomes invisible. It
seems—upon the whole—less probable that
Homer drew either of these accomplishments
from the actual human life about him, than
from simple consciousness that it would be very
gratifying if men could do these things. And,
indeed, as touches enduring art, to write
"with the eye upon the object" appears a rela-
tively modern pretence, perhaps not uncon-
nected with the coetaneous phrase of "all my
eye."

Then, when the Attic drama came to flower-
age, the actors were masked, so that their features might display unhuman perfection; and
were mounted upon cothurni, to lend impres-
siveness to man's physical mediocrity; and
were clothed in draperies which philanthropic-
ally eclipsed humanity's frugal graces. In
painting or sculpture, where the human body
could be idealized with a free hand, the Greek

rule was nakedness: in drama, where the artist's material was incorrigible flesh, there was nothing for it save to disguise the uncaptivating groundwork through some discreet employment of fair apparel. Thus only could the audience be hoodwinked into forgetting for a while what men and women really looked like. So in drama Theseus declaimed in imperial vestments, and in sculpture wore at the very most a fig-leaf. It is hardly necessary to point out that the Greeks shared few of our delusions concerning "decency": for, of course, they had no more moral aversion to a man's appearing naked in the street than to a toad's doing so, and objected simply on the ground that both were ugly. So they resolutely wrote about—and carved and painted, for that matter—men "as they ought to be" doing such things as it would be gratifying for men to do if these feats were humanly possible. . . And in the twilit evening of Greek literature you will find Theocritus clinging with unshaken ardor to unreality, and regaling the townfolk of Alexandria with tales of an improbable Sicily, where the inhabitants are on terms of friendly intimacy with cyclopes, water-nymphs and satyrs.

Equally in the Middle Ages did literature avoid deviation into the credible. When carpets of brocade were spread in April meadows it was to the end that barons and ladies might listen with delight to peculiarly unplausible accounts of how Sire Roland held the pass at Roncevaux single-handed against an army, and of Lancelot's education at the bottom of a pond by elfin pedagogues, and of how Virgil builded Naples upon eggshells. When English-speaking tale-tellers began to concoct homespun romances they selected such themes as Bevis of Southampton's addiction to giant-killing, and Guy of Warwick's encounter with a man-eating cow eighteen feet long, and the exploits of Thomas of Reading, who exterminated an infinity of dragons and eloped with Prester John's daughter after jilting the Queen of Fairyland. Chaucer, questionless, was so injudicious as to dabble in that muddy stream of contemporaneous happenings which time alone may clarify: but the parts of Chaucer that endure are a Knight's story of mythological events, a Prioress's unsubstantiated account of a miracle, a Nun's Priest's anticipation of Rostand's barnyard fantasy, and a ream or two of other delightful flimflams. From his contemporaries Chaucer got such matter as the Miller's tale of a clerk's misadventures in osculation.

4

But with the invention of printing, thoughts spread so expeditiously that it became possible to acquire quite serviceable ideas without the trouble of thinking: and very few of us since then have cared to risk impairment of our minds by using them. A consequence was that, with inaction, man's imagination in general grew more sluggish, and demurred, just as mental indolence continues to balk, over the exertion of conceiving an unfamiliar *locale,* in any form of art. The deterioration, of course, was gradual, and for a considerable while theatrical audiences remained receptively illiterate. And it seems at first sight gratifying to note that for a lengthy period Marlowe was the most "popular" of the Elizabethan playwrights: for in Marlowe's superb verse there is really very little to indicate that the writer had ever encountered any human beings, and certainly nothing whatever to show that he had seriously considered this especial division of fauna: whereas all his scenes are laid somewhere a long way west of the Hesperides. Yet Marlowe's popularity, one cannot but suspect, was furthered by unæsthetic aids, in divers "comic" scenes which time has beneficently destroyed. At all events, complaisant dramatists, out of a normal preference for butter with their daily bread, soon began to romance about contemporary life. It is not Shakespeare's least claim to applause that he sedulously avoided doing anything of the sort. To the other side, being human, Shakespeare was not untainted by the augmenting trend toward "realism", and in depicting his fellows was prone to limit himself to exaggeration of their powers of fancy and diction. This, as we now know, is a too sparing employment of untruthfulness: and there is ground for sharp arraignment of the imbecility attributed to Lear, and Othello, and Hamlet, and Macbeth, and Romeo —to cite only a few instances,—by any candid estimate of their actions, when deprived of the transfiguring glow wherewith Shakespeare invests what is being done, by evoking a haze of lovely words. For really, to go mad because a hostess resents your bringing a hundred servants on a visit, or to murder your wife because she has misplaced a handkerchief, is much the sort of conduct which is daily chronicled by the morning-paper; and in charity to man's self-respect should be restricted to the ostentatious impermanence of journalism. But at bottom Shakespeare never displayed any very hearty admiration for humanity as a race, and would seem to have found not many more commendable traits in general exercise among mankind than did the authors of the Bible.

Few of the art-reverencing Elizabethans, however, handled the surrounding English life: when they dealt with the contemporaneous it was with a reassuringly remote Italian background, against which almost anything might be supposed to happen, in the way of picturesque iniquity and poisoned wine: so that they composed with much of that fine irresponsibility wherewith American journalists expose the court-life of Madrid. But the Jacobean drama tended spasmodically toward untruths about its audience's workaday life, with such depressing results as *Hyde Park, The Roaring Girl* and *The New Inn*, by men who in the field of unrestricted imagination had showed themselves to be possessed of genuine ability.

5

Then came the gallant protest of the Restoration, when Wycherley and his successors
in drama, commenced to write of contemporary
life in much the spirit of modern musical comedy, which utilizes a fac-simile of the New
York Pennsylvania Railway Station, or of the
Capitol at Washington, as an appropriate
setting for a ballet and a comedian's colloquy
with the orchestra leader. Thus here the scenes
are in St. James's Park, outside Westminster,
in the New Exchange, and in other places
familiar to the audience; and the characters
barter jokes on current events: but the laws
of the performers' mimic existence are frankly
extra-mundane, and their antics, in Restoration
days as now, would have subjected them to immediate arrest upon the auditorial side of footlights. A great deal of queer nonsense has
been printed concerning the comedy of Gallantry, upon the startling assumption that its
authors copied the life about them. It is true
that Wycherley, in this the first of English
authors to go astray, began the pernicious
practise of depicting men as being not very

much better than they actually are: of that I
will speak later: but Wycherley had the saving
grace to present his men and women as trammeled by the social restrictions of Cloud-
Cuckoo-Land alone. And, were there nothing
else, it seems improbable that Congreve, say,
really believed that every young fellow spoke
habitually in terms of philosophic wit and
hated his father; and that every old hunks possessed, more or less vicariously, a beautiful
second wife; and that people married without
licenses, or, indeed, without noticing very particularly whom they were marrying; and that
monetary competence and happiness and all-
important documents, as well as a sudden turn
for heroic verse, were regularly accorded to
everybody toward eleven o'clock in the evening.

6

Thus far the illiterate ages, when as yet so
few persons could read that literature tended
generally toward the acted drama. The stage
could supply much illusory assistance, in the
way of pads and wigs and grease-paints and
soft lightings, toward making men appear heroic and women charming: but, after all, the
rôles were necessarily performed by human

34

beings, and the charitable deceit was not continuous. The audience was ever and anon being reminded, against its firm-set will, that men were mediocre creatures.

Nor could the poets, however rapidly now multiplied their verse-books, satisfactorily delude their patrons into overlooking this unpleasant fact. For one reason or another, men as a whole have never taken kindlily to printed poetry: most of us are unable to put up with it at all, and even to the exceptional person verse after an hour's reading becomes unaccountably tiresome. Prose—for no very patent cause—is much easier going. So the poets proved ineffectual comforters, who could but rarely be-drug even the few to whom their charms did not seem gibberish.

With the advent of the novel, all this was changed. Not merely were you relieved from metrical fatigue, but there came no commonplace flesh-and-blood to give the lie to the artist's pretensions. It was possible, really for the first time, acceptably to present in literature men "as they ought to be." Richardson could dilate as unrestrainedly as he pleased upon the super-eminence in virtue and sin, respectively, of his Grandison and his Lovelace emboldened by the knowledge that there was nothing to check him off save the dubious touchstone of his reader's common-sense. Fielding was not only able to conduct a broad-shouldered young ruffian to fortune and a lovely wife, but could moreover endow Tom Jones with all sorts of heroic and estimable qualities such as (in mere unimportant fact) rascals do not display in actual life. When the novel succeeded the drama it was no longer necessary for the artist to represent human beings with even partial veracity: and this new style of writing at once became emblematic.

And so it has been ever since. Novelists have severally evolved their pleasing symbols wherewith approximately to suggest human beings and the business of human life, much as remote Egyptians drew serrated lines to convey the idea of water and a circle to indicate eternity. The symbols have often varied: but there has rarely been any ill-advised attempt to depict life as it seems in the living of it, or to crystallize the vague notions and feeble sensations with which human beings, actually, muddle through to an epitaph; if only because all sensible persons, obscurely aware that this routine is far from what it ought to be, have

always preferred to deny its existence. And
moreover, we have come long ago to be guided
in any really decisive speech or action by what
we have read somewhere; and so, may fairly
claim that literature should select (as it does)
such speeches and such actions as typical of
our essential lives, rather than the gray inter-
stices, which we perforce fill in extempore, and
botch.

As concerns the novelists of the day before
yesterday, this evasion of veracity is already
more or less conceded: the "platitudinous he-
roics" of Scott and the "exaggerated senti-
mentalism" of Dickens are notorious in quite
authoritative circles whose *ducdame* is the honest belief that art is a branch of pedagogy.
Thackeray, as has been pointed out elsewhere,
avoids many a logical outcome of circumstance,
when recognition thereof would be inconvenient,
by killing off somebody and blinding the reader
with a tear-drenched handkerchief. And when
we sanely appraise the most cried-up writer of
genteel "realism", matters are not conducted
much more candidly. Here is a fair sample:—
"From the very beginning of my acquaintance
with you, your manners, impressing me with
the fullest belief of your arrogance, your con-

ceit, and your selfish disdain of the feelings of others, were such as to form that groundwork of disapprobation on which succeeding events have built so immovable a dislike, and I had not known you a month before I felt that you were the last man in the world whom I could ever be prevailed on to marry." It is Miss Austen's most famous, most beloved, and most "natural" character replying—not by means of a stilted letter, but colloquially, under the stress of emotion—to a proposal of marriage by the man she loves. This is a crisis which in human life a normal young woman simply does not meet with any such rhetorical architecture. . . So there really seems small ground for wonder that Mr. Darcy observed, "You have said quite enough, madam"; and no cause whatever for surprise that he hastily left the room, and was heard to open the front-door and quit the house. . . Yet, be it forthwith added, Scott and Dickens and Thackeray, and even Miss Austen, were in the right, from one or another æsthetic standpoint, in thus variously editing and revising their contemporaries' unsatisfactory disposition of life. Indeed, upon no plea could they be bound to emulate malfeasance.

Criticism as to the veracity of more recent writers is best dismissed with the well-merited commendation that novelists to-day continue rigorously to respect the Second Commandment. Meanwhile it may, with comparative safety, be pointed out that no interred writer of widely conceded genius has ever displayed in depicting the average of human speech and thought and action, and general endowments, such exactness as would be becoming in an affidavit; but rather, when his art touched on these dangerous topics, has regarded romantic prevarication as a necessity. The truth about ourselves is the one truth, above all others, which we are adamantine not to face. And this determination springs, not wholly from vanity, but from a profound race-sense that by such denial we have little to lose, and a great deal to gain.

7

For, as has been said before, an inveterate Sophocles notes clearly that veracity is the one unpardonable sin, not merely against art, but against human welfare. . . . You will observe that the beginnings of fiction everywhere, among all races, take with curious unanimity the same form. It is always the history of the unlooked-for achievements and the ultimate very public triumph of the ill-used youngest son. From the myth of Zeus, third son of Chronos, to the third prince of the fairy-tale, there is no exception. Everywhere it is to the despised weakling that romance accords the final and very public victory. For in the life-battle for existence it was of course the men of puniest build who first developed mental ability, since hardier compeers, who took with bloodied hands that which they wanted, had no especial need of less reliable makeshifts: and everywhere this weakling, quite naturally, afforded himself in imagination what the force of circumstance denied him in fact. Competent persons, then as now, had neither the time nor ability for literature.

By and bye a staggering stroke of genius improved the tale by adding the handicap of sex-weakness: and Cinderella (whom romance begot and deified as Psyche) straightway led captive every dreamer's hitherto unvoiced desire. This is the most beloved story in the world's library, and, barring a tremendous exception to which I shall presently return, will always remain without rival. Any author any-

40

where can gain men's love by remodeling (not too drastically) the history of Cinderella: thousands of calligraphic persons have, of course, availed themselves of this fortunate circumstance: and the seeming miracle is that the naïve and the most sophisticated continue to thrill, at each re-telling of the hackneyed story, with the instant response of fiddlestrings, to an interpretation of life which one is tempted to describe as fiddlesticks. Yet an inevitable very public triumph of the downtrodden—with all imaginable pomp and fanfare—is of necessity a tenet generally acceptable to a world of ineffectual inhabitants, each one of whom is a monarch of dreams incarcerated in a prison of flesh; and each of whom is hourly fretted, no less by the indifference of nature to his plight, than by the irrelevancy thereto of those social orderings he dazedly ballots into existence. . . Christianity, with its teaching that the oppressed shall be exalted, and the unhappy made free of eternal bliss, thus came in the nick of occasion, to promise what the run of men were eager to believe. Such a delectable prospect, irrespective of its plausibility, could not in the nature of things fail to become popular: as has been strikingly attested by man's wide

41

acceptance of the rather exigent requirements of Christianity, and his honest endeavors ever since to interpret them as meaning whatever happens to be convenient.

In similar fashion, humanity would seem at an early period to have wrenched comfort from prefiguring man as the hero of the cosmic romance. For it was unpleasantly apparent that man did not excel in physical strength, as set against the other creatures of a planet whereon may be encountered tigers and elephants. His senses were of low development, as compared with the senses of insects: and, indeed, senses possessed by some of these small contemporaries man presently found he did not share, nor very clearly understand. The luxury of wings, and even the common comfort of a caudal appendage, was denied him. He walked painfully, without hoofs, and, created naked as a shelled almond, with difficulty outlived a season of inclement weather. Physically, he displayed in not a solitary trait a product of nature's more ambitious labor. . . He, thus, surpassed the rest of vital creation in nothing except, as was beginning to be rumored, the power to reason; and even so, was apparently too magnanimous to avail himself of the privilege.

But to acknowledge such disconcerting facts would never do: just as inevitably, therefore, as the peafowl came to listen with condescension to the nightingale, and the tortoise to deplore the slapdash ways of his contemporaries, man probably began very early to regale himself with flattering narratives as to his nature and destiny. ,Among the countless internecine animals that roamed earth, puissant with claw and fang and sinew, an ape reft of his tail, and grown rusty at climbing, was the most formidable, and in the end would triumph. It was of course considered blasphemous to inquire into the grounds for this belief, in view of its patent desirability, for the race was already human. So the prophetic portrait of man treading among cringing pleosauri to browbeat a frightened dinosaur was duly scratched upon the cave's wall, and art began forthwith to accredit human beings with every trait and destiny which they desiderated. . .

And so to-day, as always, we delight to hear about invincible men and women of unearthly loveliness—corrected and considerably augmented versions of our family circle,—performing feats illimitably beyond our modest powers. And so to-day no one upon the prefer-

43

able side of Bedlam wishes to be reminded of what we are in actuality, even were it possible, by any disastrous miracle, ever to dispel the mist which romance has evoked about all human doings; and to the golden twilight of which old usage has so accustomed us that, like nocturnal birds, our vision grows perturbed in a clearer atmosphere. And we have come very firmly to believe in the existence of men everywhere, not as in fact they are, but "as they ought to be".

8

Now art, like all the other noteworthy factors in this remarkable world, serves in the end utilitarian purposes. When a trait is held up as desirable, for a convincingly long while, the average person, out of self-respect, pretends to possess it: with time, he acts letter-perfect as one endowed therewith, and comes unshakably to believe that it has guided him from infancy. For while everyone is notoriously swayed by appearances, this is more especially true of his own appearance: cleanliness is, if not actually next to godliness, so far a promoter of benevolence that no man feels upon quite friendly

44

terms with his fellow-beings when conscious
that he needs a shave; and if in grief you resolutely contort your mouth into a smile you
somehow do become forthwith aware of a considerable mitigation of misery. . . . So it
is that man's vanity and hypocrisy and lack
of clear thinking are in a fair way to prove in
the outcome his salvation.

All is vanity, quoth the son of David, invert-
ing the truth for popular consumption, as became a wise Preacher who knew that vanity is
all. For man alone of animals plays the ape
to his dreams. That a dog dreams vehemently
is matter of public knowledge: it is perfectly
possible that in his more ecstatic visions he
usurps the shape of his master, and visits
Elysian pantries in human form: with awak-
ening, he observes that in point of fact he is a
dog, and as a rational animal, makes the best
of canineship. But with man the case is otherwise, in that when logic leads to any humiliating conclusion, the sole effect is to discredit
logic.

So has man's indomitable vanity made a
harem of his instincts, and walled off a seraglio
wherein to beget the virtues and refinements
and all ennobling factors in man's long prog-

ress from gorillaship. As has been suggested, creative literature would seem to have sprung simply from the instinct of any hurt animal to seek revenge,—and "to get even", as the phrase runs, in the field of imagination when such revenge was not feasible in any other arena. . . Then, too, it is an instinct common to brute creatures that the breeding or even the potential mother must not be bitten,—upon which modest basis a little by a little mankind builded the fair code of *domnei,* or woman-worship, which yet does yeoman service among legislators toward keeping half our citizens "out of the mire of politics." From the shuddering dread that beasts manifest toward uncomprehended forces, such as wind and thunder and tall waves, man developed religion, and a consoling assurance of divine paternity. And when you come to judge what he made of sexual desire, appraising the deed in view as against the wondrous overture of courtship and that infinity of high achievements which time has seen performed as grace-notes, words fail before his egregious thaumaturgy. For after any such stupendous bit of hocus-pocus, there seems to be no limit fixed to the conjurations of human vanity.

46

9

And these aspiring notions blended a great while since, into what may be termed the Chivalrous attitude toward life. Thus it is that romance, the real demiurge, the first and loveliest daughter of human vanity, contrives all those dynamic illusions which are used to further the ultimate ends of romance. . . The cornerstone of Chivalry I take to be the idea of vicarship: for the chivalrous person is, in his own eyes at least, the child of God, and goes about this world as his Father's representative in an alien country. It was very adroitly to human pride, through an assumption of man's personal responsibility in his tiniest action, that Chivalry made its appeal; and exhorted every man to keep faith, not merely with the arbitrary will of a strong god, but with himself. There is no cause for wonder that the appeal was irresistible, when to each man it thus admitted that he himself was the one thing seriously to be considered. . . So man became a chivalrous animal; and about this flattering notion of divine vicarship builded his elaborate mediæval code, to which, in essentials, a great number of persons adhere even

47

nowadays. Questionless, however, the Chivalrous attitude does not very happily fit in with modern conditions, whereby the self-elected obligations of the knight-errant toward repressing evil are (in theory at all events) more efficaciously discharged by an organized police and a jury system.

And perhaps it was never, quite, a "practical" attitude,— *mais quelle geste!* as was observed by a pre-eminently chivalrous person. At worst, it is an attitude which one finds very taking to the fancy as the posture is exemplified by divers mediæval chroniclers, who had sound notions about portraying men "as they ought to be". . . There is Nicolas de Caen, for instance, who in his *Dizain des Reines* (with which I am familiar, I confess, in the English version alone) presents with some naïveté this notion of divine vicarship, in that he would seem to restrict it to the nobility and gentry. "For royal persons and their immediate associates", Dom Nicolas assumes at outset, "are the responsible stewards of Heaven": and regarding them continuously as such, he selects from the lives of various queens ten crucial moments wherein (as Nicolas phrases it), "Destiny has thrust her sceptre into the hands of a human being, and left the weakling free to steer the pregnant outcome. Now prove thyself to be at bottom a god or else a beast, saith Destiny, and now eternally abide that choice.'' Yet this, and this alone, when you come to think of it, is what Destiny says, not merely to ''royal persons and their immediate associates'', but to everyone. . . And in his *Roman de Lusignan* Nicolas deals with that quaint development of the Chivalrous attitude to which I just alluded, that took form, as an allied but individual illusion, in *domnei,* or woman-worship; and found in a man's mistress an ever-present reminder, and sometimes a rival, of God. There is something not unpathetic in the thought that this once world-controlling force is restricted to-day to removing a man's hat in an elevator and occasionally compelling a surrender of his seat in a streetcar. . . . But this *Roman de Lusignan* also has been put into English, with an Afterword by the translator wherein the theories of *domnei* are rather painstakingly set forth: and thereto I shall presently recur, for further consideration of this illusion of *domnei.*

Throughout, of course, the Chivalrous attitude was an intelligent attitude, in which one spun romances and accorded no meticulous attention to mere facts. . . For thus to spin romances is to bring about, in every sense, man's recreation, since man alone of animals can, actually, acquire a trait by assuming, in defiance of reason, that he already possesses it. To spin romances is, indeed, man's proper and peculiar function in a world wherein he only of created beings can make no profitable use of the truth about himself. For man alone of animals plays the ape to his dreams. So he fares onward chivalrously, led by *ignes fatui* no doubt, yet moving onward. And that the goal remains ambiguous seems but a trivial circumstance to any living creature who knows, he knows not how, that to stay still can be esteemed a virtue only in the dead.

10

Indeed, when I consider the race to which I have the honor to belong, I am filled with respectful wonder. . . All about us flows and gyrates unceasingly the material universe,—an endless inconceivable jumble of rotatory blazing gas and frozen spheres and detonating comets, wherethrough spins Earth like a frail midge. And to this blown molecule adhere what millions and millions and millions of parasites just such as I am, begetting and dreaming and slaying and abnegating and toiling and making mirth, just as did aforetime those countless generations of our forebears, every one of whom was likewise a creature just such as I am! Were the human beings that have been subjected to confinement in flesh each numbered, as is customary in other penal institutes, with what interminable row of digits might one set forth your number, say, or mine?

Nor is this everything. For my reason, such as it is, perceives this race, in its entirety, in the whole outcome of its achievement, to be beyond all wording petty and ineffectual: and no more than thought can estimate the relative proportion to the material universe of our poor Earth, can thought conceive with what quintillionths to express that fractional part which I, as an individual parasite, add to Earth's negligible fretting by ephemeræ.

And still—behold the miracle!—still I believe life to be a personal transaction between myself and Omnipotence; I believe that what I do is somehow of importance; and I believe that I am on a journey toward some very public triumph not unlike that of the third prince in the fairy-tale. . . Even to-day I believe in this dynamic illusion. For that creed was the first great inspiration of the demiurge,—man's big romantic idea of Chivalry, of himself as his Father's representative in an alien country;—and it is a notion at which mere fact and reason yelp denial unavailingly. For every one of us is so constituted that he knows the romance to be true, and corporal fact and human reason in this matter, as in divers others, to be the suborned and perjured witnesses of "realism".

III

THE WITCH-WOMAN

—You are a terrible, delicious woman! begotten on a water-demon, people say. I ask no questions. . . .

—And so you do not any longer either love or hate me, Perion?

—It was not I who loved you, but a boy that is dead now. . . .

—Yet I loved you, Perion—oh, yes, in part I loved you. . . .

—So that to-day I walk with ghosts, king's daughter: and I am none the happier. . . .

—It was not for nothing that Pressina was my mother, and I know many things, pilfering light from the past to shed it upon the future.

—Roman de Lusignan

III

Which Hints At the Witch Woman

YOU perceive, then, it is by the grace of romance that man has been exalted above the other animals. It was by romance, in a fashion I have endeavored to make clear, that mankind was endowed with all its virtues: so we need hardly be surprised that to romance mankind has likewise had to repair in search of vices. Here, though, the demiurge would seem to have been not quite so successful, perhaps because men lacked the requisite inborn capacity to attain any real distinction in wickedness. . . Indeed, I question whether wickedness is possible to humanity outside of literature. In books, of course, may be encountered any number of competently evil people, who take a proper pride in their depravity. But in life men go wrong without dignity, and sin as it were from hand to mouth. In life wrongdoing seems deplorably prone to take form either as a business necessity or as a public nuisance, and in each avatar is shunned by the considerate person.

Yes, in life the "wicked" people are rather pitiable, and quite hopelessly tedious as associates. I suspect that the root of most evil is, not so much the love of money, as the lack of imagination: and few in fact deny that our recognized "criminals" are the victims of mental inability to contrive and carry through this or that infringement of the civil code in precisely the unobtrusive fashion of our leading captains of industry. Yet the romantic have always fabled that by whole-hearted allegiance to evil this life in the flesh—by "jumping", as the Thane of Cawdor put it, any possible life to come,—might be rendered vastly more entertaining, and might even afford to the sinner control of superhuman powers. Men have always dreamed thus of evading the low levels of everyday existence, and of augmenting their inadequate natural forces, by entering into some formal compact with evil. Hence have arisen the innumerable legends of sorcerers and witches, and the disfigurement of history with divers revolting chapters relative to the martyrdom of half-witted old women so injudicious as to maintain a cat. And toward

56

such chapters it seems needful momentarily to digress, by very briefly indicating certain vulgar notions about the witch-woman, so as to make clear what I have in mind as to another dynamic illusion; and needful, too, to speak of these chapters with flippant levity, because such enormities grow unbearable when regarded seriously. . .

2

Witchcraft, if it were not indeed the first manifestation of "feminism", was practised almost exclusively by women. There has been a feebly paradoxical attempt to contend that the Devil was the original witch, when he played the impostor with our primal parents, and that the serpent whose form he assumed was his imp, or familiar spirit: but the theory lacks sure corroboration, if only because the Prince of Darkness is, on venerable authority, a gentleman; and if but in this capacity, would be the first to quote that axiomatic *Place aux dames* which cynics assert to be his workaday rule.

At all events, sorcery was imputed to both the wives of Adam. Thus the Talmudists tell us how Lilith, his first helpmate,—for the then comparatively novel offence of refusing to obey her husband,—was cast out of Paradise, to be succeeded by Eve; and how since this eviction Lilith, now adulterously allied with the powers of evil, has passed her existence "in the upper regions of the air", whence she occasionally speeds earthward to seek amusement in the molestation of infants. She it is who cunningly tortures the descendants of her unforgiven husband with croup and the pangs of teething. Sheer pedantry tempts one to point out here that it was on this account the Hebrew mothers were accustomed, when putting their children to sleep, to sing *"Lullaby!"* which is when Englished "Lilith, avaunt!" so that all our cradle-songs are the results of a childless marriage.

Equally in Jewish legend has Lilith's successor, our joint grandmother Eve, been accredited with being a trifle prone to sorcerous practises. I regret that the details as thus rumored are not very nicely quotable: but they seem quite as well authenticated as any other gossip of the period: so that witchcraft may fairly be declared the first invention of the first woman. Eve had dealings with the Devil some while before the birth of Cain, even before the incident of the fig-leaves. She was

58

a magician before she was a mother, and conjuring with her took precedence of costume. And while the fact that forever after there were twenty women given to witchcraft as against one man, may seem a little strange, King James the First of England, in his *Demonology*, explains it, speciously enough, by yet another reference to the most ancient of all scandals. "The reason is easy, for as that sex is frailer than man is, so it is easier to be entrapped by the gross snares of the Devil, as was over-well proved by the serpent's beguiling deceit of Eve at the beginning, which makes him the homelier with that sex." In other words, King James is bold enough to voice it as a truism that women go to the Devil in search of congeniality.

3

Men have always inclined instead to sorcery. A witch, it may be premised, derived her power from a contract with the especial devil to whom she became in some sort a servant: whereas a sorcerer commanded divers spirits in bale, by means of his skill at magic, and in this ticklish traffic was less the servant than the master.

And the foremost of all sorcerers was probably Johan Faustus of Würtemburg. He certainly stays the best known, now that Goethe and Gounod and Berlioz and so many others have had their fling at him, as an alluring peg whereon to hang librettoes and allegories. But it is Christopher Marlowe's version of the legend which to-day would seem almost to justify any conceivable practises, however diabolic, without which we had lacked this masterwork of loveliness. Presently I must speak of this drama at greater length, and of Marlowe too, as one of those neglected geniuses with which the British branch of American literature has been so undeservedly favored. . .

4

Momentarily waiving art's debt to conjurers, and returning to their sister practitioners, the typical witch-woman was distinguishable—according to Gaule, in his *Select Cases of Conscience Touching Witches and Witchcraft,*—by "a wrinkled face, a furred brow, a hairy lip, a gobber tooth, a squint eye, a squeaking voice, and a scolding tongue." These were the outward marks of a sinister genus, which was divided into three species. Thus antiquity distinguished thereamong "white witches", who could help, but not hurt; "black witches", who could hurt, but not help; and "gray witches", who could do either at will. All were persecuted with severity, which seems natural enough in harrying black or even gray witches, but rather unaccountable when exercised toward the beneficent white witch. It appears, however, that the last were not without their human frailties: Dryden at least refers to someone as being as little honest as he could manage, and "like white witches mischievously good." Then, too, a Jacobean publicist has left it on record that "it were a thousand times better for the land if all witches, but especially the blessing witch, might suffer death. For men do commonly hate and spit at the damnifying sorceress as unworthy to live among them: whereas they flee unto the other in necessity, they depend upon her as their god, and by this means thousands are carried away to their final confusion. Death, therefore, is the just and deserved portion of the good witch." Such logic smacks of sophistry, but remoter times found it acceptable.

Gray witches also, as has been said, were by way of being philanthropists. Of this species were the famed Lapland witches, from whom of old the visiting sailors purchased favorable winds. Their traffic had at worst the merit of simplicity: the customer received a cord in which were tied three knots; on untying the first arose an auspicious breeze, on loosing the second a stronger gale, whereas meddling with the third evoked a storm sufficient to wreck the staunchest vessel. Pomponius Mela tells of a company of priestesses in the Island of Sena, off the coast of Gaul, possessed of similar power to trouble the sea and control the winds, but able to direct their amendments of natural laws solely toward the benefit of such as sought their help. And Randulph Higden, in his *Polychronicon,* states that the witches in the Isle of Man dealt with the mariners of his time in much the same manner. Before the days of steam and electricity this traffic in wind supplied international wants: and it has been profanely asserted that many of our most eminent statesmen are over-mindful of precedent.

The Witches' Sabbat, my friend Richard Harrowby informs me, was "traditionally a meeting attended by all witches in satisfactory diabolical standing, lightly attired in smears of various magical ointments: and their vehicle of transportation to these outings was of course the traditional broomstick. Good Friday night was the favorite time for such gatherings, which were likewise held after dusk on St. John's Eve, on Walburga's Eve, and on Hallowe'en Night. The diversions were numerous: there was feasting, with somewhat unusual fare, and music and dancing, with the Devil performing obligatos on the pipes or a cittern, and not infrequently preaching a burlesque sermon. He usually attended in the form of a monstrous goat; and—when not amorously inclined,—often thrashed the witches with their own broomsticks. The more practical pursuits of the evening included the opening of graves, to despoil dead bodies of finger- or toe-joints, and portions of the winding-sheet, with which to prepare a powder that had strange uses. . . But the less said of that, the better. Here, also, the Devil taught his disciples how to make and christen statues of clay or wax, so that by roasting these effigies the persons whose names they bore would be wasted away by sickness.''

While persecuting anyone, witches were visible to their victims alone: and to the latter were recommended divers methods of self-protection. Thus conceded authorities suggested taking the wall of the witch in a town or street, and in rural circumstances passing to the right of her. In passing, one was invariably to clench both hands, with thumbs doubled beneath the fingers: and it was thought well to salute every known witch civilly before she spoke, and on no account to accept a present from her. To draw blood from a witch forthwith rendered her enchantments ineffectual. Moreover, a horseshoe nailed to the threshold of a door was well known to hinder the power of any witch from entering the house.

Persons accused of witchcraft could be proven guilty in various ways: there was never any popular demand for acquittal. Sometimes conviction was secured by finding on their bodies certain marks, of which prudishness prevents any description: by another process the suspected woman was required—and if sorcerously given was unable—to repeat the Lord's Prayer. A variant test was based on the belief that, in the unchivalrous phrasing of King James, "witches cannot shed tears, though women in general are, like the crocodile, ready to weep upon every light occasion." Other authorities asserted that a witch can as a matter of fact shed three tears, but no more, and these only from the left eye. . . The most popular ordeal, at all events, was that of "swimming" the suspected witch. By this method she was stripped naked, and cross-bound, with the right thumb fastened to the left toe and the left thumb to the right toe; and was thus cast into a pond or river, to choose between the alternatives of drowning and thereby attesting her innocence, or of struggling to keep above the water in order to be burned as a convicted witch. "For it appears"—again King James is cited—"that God hath appointed for a supernatural sign for the impiety of witches that the water shall refuse to receive into her bosom all these that have shaken off them the sacred waters of baptism, and have wilfully refused the benefit thereof". . .

It was long an unquestioned belief that certain persons were peculiarly endowed with the faculty of distinguishing witches from the rest of humanity. Of these "witch-finders" the most celebrated was that Matthew Hopkins who during the seventeenth century was officially employed for this purpose by the English government. Hopkins was in his time a personage, and an unexcelled detector of the "special

marks'' which are the sure signs of a witch.
But his customary test was to ''swim'' the
accused. By this really infallible method of
furnishing public recreation he averaged sixty
murders to the year; and was thriving in his
unique profession when it somehow occurred
to someone to put Hopkins himself to Hopkins'
test. The sequel is cheering: for he impru-
dently remained above water, and being thus
by his own methods proven a witch, was burned
alive. . .

5

It seems a great while ago that such things
were possible. We have relinquished nowadays
our belief in witchcraft, along with our faith
in a many other Biblical matters. The faith
of every century is, however, the natural
laughing-stock of its immediate successors. So
it is now very generally conceded that witches
are obsolete, and that the cause of evil is to-day
furthered by more competent factors, such as
denying the ballot to women, or not restricting
alcohol as a poison to the communion-table,
or whatever other prevalent arrangement especially evokes the speaker's natural talents for
being irrational.

Yet consideration suggests that many witches have a more plausible title to existence than falls to most of their deriders. Were it but for the noble aid which certain sorceresses have rendered to romance, it must be that somewhere, or east of the sun or west of the moon, there is a Paradise of Witches, wherein all these abide eternally. There stands the house of Pamphile, whom Lucius saw transformed into an owl, and by whose pilfered unguents he himself was disastrously converted into an ass. In the moonlit court-yard glitters an ever-moving wheel, barley and laurel burn together there, and Simætha calls to the bright and terrible lady of heaven for pity and help and vengeance. Near-by a nameless red-haired witch waits at the vine-hung opening of a cave: in her hand is a spray of blossoming hemlock: and she cries, "What d'ye lack? It has a price." By the road-side, on the marge of a clear pool a woman smiles to think of that which she alone foresees, with bright wild eyes that are as changeless as the eyes of a serpent: for this is Lamia; and Lycius has already left Corinth. On the adjoining heath the three Weird Sisters stir their cauldron: they are observed, from a respectful distance, by that

Madge Gray who once rifled the rectory larder
at Tappington, and by that wee Nannie,
"Cutty-Sark", who in the dance at Kirk-
Alloway extorted injudicious applause from
Tam O'Shanter. Off shore Parthenope and
Ligeia and Leucosia, the dreaded Sirens,
chaunt their endless song: fathoms beneath
them that other sea-witch, with whom the little
mermaid trafficked, lurks in a horrible forest
of polypi, and caresses meditatively a fat drab-
colored water-snake. Through yonder glen
whirls the blasphemous carnival of Walpurgis,
no more sedate to-night than when Faustus
spied upon it very anciently. Beyond those
dense thickets one may yet come to the many-
columned palace, builded of polished stones,
wherein Circe waits the coming of unwary
mariners,—Circe, the fair-haired and delicate-
voiced witch, who is a bane to men, and yet
sometimes takes mortal lovers. . .

6

But here we enter dreamland. Thus far a
little pedantic levity has seemed permissible
enough, in treating of man's dealings with the
witch-woman as his conscience prompted, since
here as elsewhere a high moral motive has been

the banner flown by such enormities as grow
unbearable when regarded seriously. But the
dreams of man arise from deeper requirements
than prompt his deeds. In dreams man has
shown no aversion to the witch-woman, whom
in his dreams he has never really confounded
with those broomstick-riding, squint-eyed and
gobber-toothed wives of the Goat that were conscientiously hunted down and murdered; but,
to the contrary, man has always clung, with
curious tenacity, to the notion of some day
attaining the good graces of that fair-haired
and delicate-voiced witch who is a bane to men,
and yet sometimes takes mortal lovers. The
aspiration was familiar even in Plutarch's far-
off heyday: and you will find that he, precise
fellow, though speaking guardedly enough of
"those very ancient fables which the Phrygians
have received and still recount of Attis, the
Bithynians of Herodotus, and the Arcadians
of Endymion", yet ventures into diffident and
delicate dissent from certain tenets of the "wise
Egyptians". . .

Always people have whispered of heroes,
strangely favored, that have won, through ob-
scure by-paths, to the witch-woman's embraces,
and by her shrewd counsel have been enabled

to excel in earthly affairs. The rumor is ubiquitous. Greek Odysseus, doubly fortunate, was thus ambiguously cherished both by Circe and by Calypso; Roman Numa Pompilius, by the Arician nymph Egeria; Cossack Ivan by the Sun's Sister, Scandinavian Helgi Thorirson by Injiborg, and Irish Oisin by golden-haired Niamh, and Scottish Thomas of Ercildoune by the Queen of Faëry: as was the French Ogier le Danois by King Arthur's elfin sister, in her hushed island realm of Avalon, and the German Tannhäuser by the furtive Aphrodite of Thuringia, in the corridors of her hollow mountain. Then there is hardly an ancient family which does not trace from Dame Mélusine (who founded the proud house of Lusigan), as well as from that more pestiferous witch-wife who was so disastrously won very long ago by Foulques Plantagenet. To all such legends the Rosicrucians, in particular, affixed a perturbing commentary. . .

In every land men have thus reported, not very gallantly, that a possible reward for surpassing the run of men in wit and strength and daring was to obtain in marriage a creature indescribably more fine and wise than a woman. Everywhere men have hungered for the witch-woman who mysteriously abides, as did Circe and Mélusine and all that whispered-of sorority, in a secluded land which is always less glaringly lighted than our workaday world shows at noontide; who is as much more shrewd as more lovely than the daughters of men; to whom all human concernments with good and evil are negligible matters, viewed much as men themselves in going about a barnyard are moved to regard the bravery and maternal devotion and thievery and incest of their fowls; and whose caresses—this above all,—awaken no satiety. . . And through desire of the witch-woman many and many a man is hinted (in those queer vague tales to which chroniclers allude with visible circumspection, and none has ever narrated quite explicitly) to have sacrificed the kindly ties of ordinary life, and finally life itself. Ubiquitous is this secretive whispering of the witch-woman's favors, that are purchased by bodily and spiritual ruin, sometimes, and even so are not too dearly bought: for everywhere is rumored thus the story of the witch-woman, and of her ageless allure, and of her inevitable elusion at the last of all her lovers, whether crowned or cassocked or ink-stained, who are but mortal. . .

Here is no place to deal with an hypothesis which alone would seem, quite, to explain this race-belief. That superhuman beings, imperceptible to everyday sense, at times, for their own veiled purposes, seek union with men, and that this union is sometimes consummated, may appear to the majority very like moonstruck fustian. Meanwhile that which men vaguely describe as "science" is slowly veering—if but by means of "new" theories concerning a fourth dimension, curved time, curved space and kindred speculations,—to the quaint finding that many cast-by superstitions of the Rosicrucians lie just ahead, and bid fair once more to be "discovered". Indeed, the common-sense, or Ptolemaic, viewpoint, which disposed of the universe without any nonsense, by looking at the earth and seeing for yourself that it was flat,—and by watching the sun and moon and stars visibly climbing one side of the sky to descend the other, while you had only to feel the ground to prove it was quite motionless,—appears to be, in one or two minor points, not infallible. And any protestation of judging all things "sensibly", now that the senses are convicted liars, seems less a boast than a confession.

8

Hypotheses apart, men believed in the witch-woman through a need far deeper than a tepid preference for veracity. For all men had loved; and most of them wooed not unsuccessfully, at one time or another, and saw what came of it: and they simply did not choose to accept the result as being anything but an exceptional and probably unique instance of something having gone wrong. With other husbands, they doggedly reflected, the case was in all likelihood quite different. . .

Against the institution of marriage has been directed, by and large, a net amount of adverse criticism such as was never attracted by any other business arrangement. Too ardent novelists, in particular, have overdone their contributions to the epithalamia of backbiting. Some rousing call to take a part therein would seem to sound as clear to the upliftingly lachrymose tale-tellers, whose imaginary wives and husbands can "grow really to know each other" only after the bank fails or some other material misfortune has reduced them to poverty and caresses, as to those fearless fictionists whose heroines find it a married woman's first duty in life to set up housekeeping with a bachelor. Indeed, the more advanced novelists nowadays are almost as contemptuous about marriage as was formerly St. Paul. The considerate philosopher hesitates, amid all this abuse, to concede that marriage, when the contracting parties are sincerely in love with each other, ends of necessity in disappointment. But this there appears to be no denying. For love too is a dynamic illusion which romance induces in order to further the labor of the demiurge, and marriage is an estate wherein illusion quite inevitably perishes.

You may marry through any motive less exalted, from desire of money or of children or of someone to do the darning, and have at least a chance of attaining the prize in view. But in love-matches there is no such chance: for, were there nothing else, love accredits the beloved with opulence in qualities which human beings display, if at all, in exiguous traces; and is compounded in large part of an awed reverence such as it is impossible to retain for any human being with intimacy. These phantoms vanish at the dawn of married life: and the most obtuse of couples set about joint house-holding with, as concerns each other, very few misapprehensions outliving the wedding-trip; for that by ordinary is a transmuting journey, upon which demi-gods depart, and wherefrom return only Mr. and Mrs. So-and-so. Now human nature, whatever cynics may assert, is humble-minded enough to think rather poorly of itself when manifested by its associates. In a love-match human nature most certainly is uplifted to the point of anticipating something better. . . And afterward you get on fairly well: you miss her to a decorous degree in absence, you do not verbally quarrel when together, and you even discover in the woman a number of admirable and quite unsuspected traits. In fact, you would as willingly part with your right hand as part with her: but then, when all is said, you are not in love with your right hand, either. And you very often wonder what has become of that other woman, whom you thought you were marrying.

9

Perhaps not many of us, however, marry for love. Love is, indeed, the one dynamic illusion that rather frequently results in impotence.

The demiurgic spirit of romance hoodwinks humanity through this dynamic illusion known as love, in order that humanity may endure, and the groans of a lover be perpetuated in the wails of an infant; to each of us in our prime "it is granted to love greatly, and to know at least one hour of pure magnanimity": yet that hour tends for no plain reason to be sterile: the madness of love-making passes like a tinted mist; and generation after generation casts its rice upon marriages which are prompted by some motive other than a mutual infatuation, and result excellently. . . . For there comes about some impediment, through the operation of our man-made social laws, so that, for one reason or another, where we love to our uttermost we do not marry. And so, we are spared the shame of seeing the highest passion which we have known, brought to nothing through the attrition of everyday life. We are permitted to believe that with favoring luck we might have retained forever the magnanimity which youth and love once briefly loaned; and we preserve a measure of self-esteem. . . Even where love-marriages are consummated, I suspect that few are prompted by the one love of either participant's life:

concerning women no married man, of course, would care to speak assuredly as touches this or any other matter; but when the perturbed bridegroom approaches the chancel he is spared at least the fear that those delectable girls whom at various times he has desired to meet there may all be awaiting him. . . And so, the husband has always a missed chance or two to embroider in reverie. . .

10

For in youth all men that live have been converts, if but in transitory allegiance, to that religion of the world's youth,—to the creed of which I spoke just now as *domnei,* or woman-worship. You may remember I promised to come back to that: and it is in reality toward this creed of *domnei* all these notions as to the witch-woman approach. . . . Thus—as I remember to have read in the English version of that *Roman de Lusignan* to which I just referred,—"it was a canon of *domnei,* it was the very essence of *domnei,* that the woman one loves is providentially set between her lover's apprehension and God, as the mobile and vital image and corporeal reminder of Heaven, as a quick symbol of beauty and holiness, of purity and perfection. In her the lover views all qualities of God which can be comprehended by merely human faculties. . . And instances were not lacking in the service of *domnei* where worship of the symbol developed into a religion sufficing in itself, and became competitor with worship of what the symbol primarily represented,—such instances as have their analogues in the legend of Ritter Tannhäuser, or in Aucassin's resolve in the romance to go down into hell with 'his sweet mistress whom he so much loves', or (here perhaps most perfectly exampled) in Arnaud de Merveil's naïve declaration that whatever portion of his heart belongs to God Heaven holds in vassalage to Adelaide de Beziers''. . .

So it used to be, you may retort with a commiserating shrug. Yet even now this once dynamic illusion of chivalrous love quite inevitably invades the life of every adolescent boy, and works transient havoc; but is by ordinary so restrained and thwarted by our man-made social laws as to be evicted without leaving any lasting monuments of the tyrant's stay, in material form. The boy's beliefs, though, are not always left conformable to his estate. For at this time romance tricks each of us so cun-

ningly, in conscienceless endeavor that the man
be brought, somehow and anyhow, to the maid's
bed, that we are persuaded what romance then
promises, in the rôle of Pandarus, can really
be come by: and so firm-set is the impression
that with some of us it remains ineffaceable,
even by marriage. The average male, of course,
is very rarely at pains to ascertain his private
belief in this or any other matter, and is content to assume he thinks and feels what seems
expected of him: but here and there a man pries
curiously into his own mind. And it is he who
presently becomes the veritable "witch-
finder", after a fashion unknown to Matthew
Hopkins. . .

For such-an-one the mother of his children,
that rather likable well-meaning creature,
proves assuredly to be not at all the person
for whom, so long ago, his heart was set a-
burning: and for that very reason her shortcomings can never dim the fire, since with its
thin and vaulting ardors she is in no wise concerned. So it glows fed with hope and memory.
For such-an-one the maid waits somewhere of
whose embraces one can never tire, as in an
unforgotten vision was once revealed to him,
once for all time. Meanwhile, in moiling

through a world of blunders, he does but break
the journey where there is tolerable company,
a deal of kindly human give-and-take, and no
rapture. If but in honor, his heart stays bound
to his first and only real love, that woman of
whom one never tires. Her coming is not yet.
He can but wait sustained by his sure faith—
discreetly left unvoiced,—that some day her
glory will be apparent, and he will enter gladly
into her secret kingdom, and will find her
kisses all that in youth he foreknew to be not
impossible. . . And meanwhile this prescience,
somehow, informs all art, just as life animates
the body, and makes art to him a vital thing.
For here and there art's masterworks become
precursors of the witch-woman's advent, and
whisper of a loveliness, as yet withheld, which
"never waxes old",—of a loveliness which
stays as yet the nebulous goal of art's surmise,
but will be obvious at the witch-woman's coming, incarnate in soft flesh; and will be no
longer impalpable as in verse, nor inarticulate
as in music, nor cataleptic as in painting. Of
this it is alone that art whispers to the veritable
"witch-finder," to the witch-woman's nympholept. And there seems to be no beauty in the
world save those stray hints of her, whose ulti-

mate revealment is not yet. . . And it is very
often through desire to express his faith in
this withheld perfection, of which he has been
conscious in broken glimpses from afar, that
he himself turns artist, and the dynamic illusion
finds secondary employment. For every art is
a confession of faith in that which is not
yet. . . Meanwhile the nympholept must wait,
contentedly enough, and share whatever happens in four-square co-partnership with another
woman, unaccountably "married" to him, and
must know at bottom that his dealings with this
other woman are temporary makeshifts. Nor
with him can there be any doubt that Methu-
selah—who was a married man,—died in this
faith.

For there is that in every human being
which demands communion with something
more fine and potent than itself. Perhaps, indeed, this is only another way of saying every
man is innately religious. . . So it befalls that
to-day, as did a many in times overpast, a few
of us yet dream of the witch-woman, and of
our meeting by and bye. . . Meanwhile it may
be that wives here and there have likewise their
disillusions and a proper sense of their own
merits. How else is one to account for the

legends of Danaë and Creusa and all those other minxes who find no husband worthy of them until a god has come down out of heaven, no less?

IV

THE ECONOMIST

—Keep out, keep out, or else you are blown up, you are dismembered, Ralph: keep out, for I am about a roaring piece of work.

—Come, what dost thou with that same book? . . . Can'st thou conjure with it?

—I can do all things easily with it: first, I can make thee drunk with ippocras at any tabern in Europe; that's one of my conjuring works.

—Our Master Parson says that's nothing. . . .

[*Enter* MEPHISTOPHILIS, *who sets squibs at their backs; and then exeunt.*]

—*The Tragical History of Dr. Faustus*

IV

Which Admires the Economist

A LL the legends I have mentioned, however, were in large part the figments of poets, so that no doubt they have been misinterpreted. For the visionary matter-of-fact people who rule the world have from the beginning misapprehended each and every matter connected with those chillingly astute persons, the poets. . . It was the penetrative common-sense of poets, as not very generally recognized, that I had in mind a few minutes ago, when I spoke of Christopher Marlowe, and referred to the *Faustus* as justifying any conceivable practises without which we had lacked this drama. You appeared at the time to think that a rather sweeping statement, but there is no question as to its truth. And in order to make this truth quite plain to you, I shall for a moment divert your attention to Christopher Marlowe, as a specific instance of what I have in mind as to another dynamic illusion. . . .

I select Marlowe as my text, from among a host of names which would serve my purpose, because Marlowe, I imagine, is to you, as through our criminal folly he is to most of us, but one of the poets in the English Literature course at college; and ranks now with chapel attendance and Greek particles and other happily outgrown annoyances. Improvident and wasteful as this is in us, I hardly wonder. No poet has been more worthily praised by more competent persons: but, for all that, Marlowe remains unappreciated, on account of our general human habit of appraising everything from irrelevant standpoints. Thus people think of Marlowe simply as a poet, whereas his real daring, like that of all the elect among creative writers, was displayed as an economist. And it is the economy of such poets that I must pause to explain.

2

Now most of the phrases which we utilize as substitutes for ideas were coined by those short-sighted persons who somehow confound economy with monetary matters: and among these from time immemorial it has been the custom to encourage the shiftless cult of mediocrity.

Age-honored precepts and all reputable proverbs concur in stating that a staid and conventional course of life should be pursued, upon the indisputable ground that this is the surest avenue to a sufficiency of creature comforts: and, indeed, if men had ever taken the corporeal circumstances of their existence very seriously people would long ago have become as indistinguishable from one another as cheesemites. Since Attica was young the "middle road" has been commended by sages and schoolmasters, by vestrymen and grandparents and bankers, and all the other really responsible constituents of society: and yet, as I need hardly point out, it has been the deviators from the highway, the strayers in by-paths and even in posted woodlands, whom men, led by instinctive wisdom, have elected to commemorate. To venture just such a mythological allusion as nowadays infuriates the reader, Clio with feminine perversity has insisted on singing the praises of those who have flown in the face of convention, and have notoriously violated every rule for securing an epitaph in which they might take reasonable pride. . . But no form of greatness is appreciable save in perspective. If your house be builded upon the side of a mountain you must leave home in order to discover the mountain's actual contour: and to a many contemporaries Homer could not but seem a beggarly street-door singer, and Jeanne Darc an ill-mannered trollop with not at all ambiguous reasons for consorting with lewd soldiers. Genius, like Niagara, is thus most majestic from a distance: and indeed, if the flights of genius are immeasurable, its descents are equally fathomless.

This would appear particularly true of that creative literary genius whereby the human brain is perverted to uses for which, as first planned against arboreal requirements, it was perhaps not especially designed. At all events, very few of our time-honored authors were esteemed as ornaments of the drawing-room, however bravely they now figure in the library; but were by the more solid element of society quite generally avoided as loose fish, on the probably Milesian analogue of their preference of other beverages to water. For, whatever one might desire the case to have been, there is really no doubt that in the production of an astoundingly large number of literary masterworks alcohol played the midwife. Equally, at first sight, the only possible way for any reputable connoisseur of art to confront this unpleasant truth was to deny its existence: and the expedient has been adopted in pedagogic circles with pleasing unanimity. The rest of us are well content to take our poets as we find them: and have no call to explain the origin of "unsubstantiated traditions" as to Shakespeare, and "calumnies of Griswold" concerning Poe, and "Bacchic myths" about Æschylos, and "the symbolic vine" of Omar, nor otherwise laboriously to cull from the sands of time a little dust to throw in our own eyes.

3

Marlowe, however, quite incontestably wasted health and repute, and even lost his life, in the pursuit of pot-house dissipation. It is unfair that, after following the onerous routine familiar to every student of poetic biography, Marlowe should be accorded no very general consideration as an economist. . . Of course few poets have escaped the charge of writing by virtue of "inspiration": and minor rhymesters, naturally enough, have fostered this balderdash, in extenuation of what they would be thought to have published under the influence of disease. But it is really too much that

Christopher Marlowe should be regarded as a dissolute wastrel afflicted with rhetorical epilepsy, during fits of which he wrote his *Hero and Leander* and his *Faustus*. Even his undeniable achievements are insidiously belittled when he is accredited with starting various hares which Shakespeare and Goethe and divers other better-winded bards ran down,—or, somewhat to jumble similes, with being the crude ore from which they extracted more or less metal, to be cast by them into enduring forms. Such belittlement is insidious, be it repeated, because this idea possesses, by ill luck, the one misleading grain of truth with which it is so difficult to deal quite justly. For it is indisputable that great poets have borrowed with a high hand from Marlowe, and—with an adroitness hereabouts distinctive of great poets,—have looked to it that where they pilfered they improved. It is equally indisputable that Christopher Marlowe was one of the supreme artists of literature.

He was an artist who labored, with sincere and appreciative reverence for his labor's worthiness, in the very highest fields of creative writing. And it is really an inconsiderable matter that his dramas are failures in that they patently do not attain to the original conception. The shortcoming is bred, not by inferior workmanship, for in technique Marlowe excelled, but by the reach of his conception, which in cold earnest was superhuman. And finally, Marlowe himself has answered this criticism, once for all, in Tamburlaine's superb rhapsody beginning *If all the pens that ever poets held,*—which I forbear to quote, because for your æsthetic enrichment it is preferable that you search out and read these thirteen lines with painstaking consideration. For thus you will come by sure knowledge of what "poetry" actually is, and must remain always. . . Indeed, as you may with profit remember, the conclusive verdict as to this tirade has been rendered by an attestedly competent judge: "In the most glorious verses now fashioned by a poet to express with subtle and final truth the supreme limit of his art, Marlowe has summed up all that can be said or thought on the office and the object, the means and the end, of this highest form of spiritual ambition." And Swinburne, for once, really appears to speak with moderation.

But I intend both here and hereafter to avoid that dreary thing called literary criticism, and make no effort to define the faults and merits of the various writers to whom I may allude. I shall not analyze, compare or appraise any of them. Instead, I shall but educe them as illustrations of my theory as to the working-code of romance, and shall consider them from that sole viewpoint. So, in deliberating the economy of Marlowe, it is eminently necessary here to emphasize the fact that his fine genius was exercised worthily. It is not unreasonable, indeed, to assert that he has had no equal anywhere. To consider—as after any such statement seems unavoidable—the possibility that, had Marlowe lived to attain maturity, he might to-day have been as tritely gabbled about as Shakespeare, is rather on a plane with debating "what song the Sirens sang" or the kindred mystery of what becomes of political issues after election. Marlowe, precisely by virtue of his more sensitive genius, was predestinate to an early death. In so far as any comparison can be carried, the advantage is, of course, with Marlowe. He was a scant two months older than Shakespeare; and all his wizardry was ended before the young fellow from Stratford had achieved anything notable. The highest aim of Shakespeare during Marlowe's lifetime was to poetize, as exactly as was humanly possible, in Marlowe's manner. It was by observing Marlowe that Shakespeare finally learned how to write: and Milton "formed himself" on the same model. Marlowe himself had no instructors, and no need of any.

To the other side, he displayed little of that gift for voicing platitudes in unforgettable terms, by virtue of which Shakespeare "comes home" to most of us, and still remains so universally quoted. Marlowe's utterance is lacking in that element of triteness without which no work of art can ever be of general appeal in a world of mostly mediocre people. Then, too, one shudders to consider what Marlowe would have made of Mercutio or Falstaff, for, *pace* Swinburne, Marlowe was really not the foremost of English humorists. To the contrary, his plays are larded with quite dreadful scenes in prose, of which the only humorous feature nowadays seems to lurk in the fact that they were intended to be amusing. In the acting, there is no doubt that such rough-and-tumble fun found appreciative audience, just as it does to-day in the athletic comedy of our Sunday newspaper cartoons, and in the screened endeavors of our most popular moving-picture actors, who to the delight of crowded auditoriums throw custard pies and fall down several flights of stairs. . . Nor may one fairly raise any question of art, this way or the other: Elizabethan dramatists labored under the necessity of making the audience laugh at certain intervals, and being unable to write comedy, Marlowe fulfilled a business obligation by concocting knockabout farce.

4

There is a deal of other calamitous printed matter bearing his name, some of which he unquestionably wrote, to his admirers' discomfort, and much of which remains gratefully dubious. Upon these productions we need waste no more time than did the writer. But it here seems necessary, even at a dire risk of appearing sophomoric, briefly to enumerate such portions of Marlowe's work as the most precise cannot conscientiously refuse to weigh, as tangible achievements which now must serve, somewhat, to counterbalance the flung-away life of a shoe-maker's oldest son.

First of course, if though but in seniority, comes *Tamburlaine the Great:* were there nothing else, the ten robustious acts of this astounding drama flow in a continuous stream of resonant verse such as has no parallel in literature, anywhere. And there is a great deal else, for the matter of the song is compact of all outlandish splendors,—a pageant, or rather a phantasmagoria, of hordes of warriors a-gleam in armor; of caliphs, viziers, bashaws, viceroys, and emirs; of naked negroes; of resplendent kings who are a little insane under the weight of their crowns; of hapless emperors imprisoned in curiously painted cages, and thus drawn about what was their kingdom yesterday, by milk-white steeds, the manes and tails of which have very carefully been dyed with men's blood; and of dream women that are more lovely than was Pygmalion's ivory girl. . . To me at least it is pleasing to note that the "comic" scenes of *Tamburlaine* (which ranked among its main attractions as an acting drama) were purposely omitted by its publisher, and so have perished, because I have always contended that there was a certain amount of latent literary taste among publishers.

The Jew of Malta is quite as far removed from any atmosphere which was ever breathed by human lungs. No doubt this play is the fiasco of a Titan, in that, having perfected his conception of Barabbas, Marlowe was not able to find him fit employment; and so, set his Jew about a rather profitless series of assassinations and poisonings. One can but remember that when Barabbas was kidnapped, stripped of all his passionate feeling for material beauty, and re-named Shylock, Shakespeare made no better work of it by involving the Israelite in silly wagers and preposterous legal quibbles, over a pound of human flesh. And meanwhile through well-nigh every speech attributed to Barabbas glints something of the bright malignity of lightning.

Then there is the *Edward the Second,* which is to some of us an annoyingly "adequate" piece of writing; more elaborately builded, and more meticulously worked out, than is habitual with the author; and yet, when all is said, containing nothing pre-eminently characteristic of Marlowe. It is a marvelous example of the "chronicle-history" play; and in superb passages it abounds: but, as a whole—even though, here again, Shakespeare found a deal he considered well worth Autolycean handling,—the drama seems to some of us not quite unique, in the high fashion of its fellows. For the persons

96

who appreciate Marlowe pay him the noble compliment of fretting over the spectacle of his doing work which merely surpasses that of other people in degree, rather than, as elsewhere, by its nature being inimitable. In short, their illogical frame of mind is not dissimilar to that in which we read, with admiring vexation, those novels of modern life that have been "charmingly written" by Mr. Maurice Hewlett.

And in that narrative poem, *Hero and Leander*, left uncompleted at his death, Marlowe revealed to Englishmen a then forgotten aspect of Grecian art,—by harking back, not to classic Greek ideals, but to the Greeks' fond and intimate scrutiny of the material world, and to exultance in the grateful form and color of lovely things when viewed precisely. It is not an ethic-ridden world he revivifies, this pleasant realm wherein beauty is the chief good of life, and life's paramount object is assumed to be that warfare in which women use not half their strength. For here it is upon bodily beauty at its perfection that Marlowe dwells, with fascinated delight. The physical charm of Hero, and every constituent of her loveliness (no less than every colorful detail of Venus's fair church of jasper-stone, which serves as appropriate framing for that loveliness), is expressed as vividly and carefully as is possible for the pen of a master craftsman: and even more deft, and more lovingly retouched, is the verbal portrait of "amorous Leander, beautiful and young". For as Marlowe here presents it, to be "beautiful and young" is, not merely the most desirable, but the unparalleled gift which life can bestow. And really, to each of us, with every dilapidating advance of time, the truth in this contention becomes no less increasingly apparent than does the necessity of concealing it. To Marlowe's finding, at any rate, wisdom and power and wealth and self-control are all very well, as the toys and solaces of maturity: but beauty in youth—being then at beauty's fullness,—alone is postulated to be worthy, less of desire, than of worship. And what men "foolishly do call virtuous" is thus relegated to a subsidiary position, in comparison with beauty, not as being in itself unimportant, but as being of no very potent value æsthetically.

Chiefly, however, the fame of Marlowe has been preserved by *The Tragical History of Dr. Faustus*. And this is actually "poetic justice", for Marlowe is at his unrivaled best in rehandling the legend of the sorcerer who, in exchange

for his soul, leased of the devil Mephistophilis
a quarter-century tenure of superhuman powers, and at the running out of his bond was
carried off alive to hell. Now it must be noted
that Marlowe thought this story as to what had
happened in Würtemberg, not quite a hundred
years before the time at which he wrote, narrated plausible and established facts. The
story told of a bargain which Marlowe believed
was capable of consummation, by such "forward wits", at the very moment Marlowe
wrote: and he no more questioned that as a
result of this bargain Johan Faustus, after
doing certain unusual things, was carried off
alive to hell than you or I would think of denying that Napoleon, after doing certain unusual
things, was carried off alive to St. Helena. But
above all, it must be noted that the exploit
which, as attributed to Faustus, most deeply
impressed Marlowe was the evocation of Helen
of Troy, in defiance of time and death, and
any process of human reason, to be the wiz-
ard's mistress. For Marlowe believed in this
feat also: and he found the man who had performed it enviable. To Marlowe—need I say?
—Queen Helen, that lost proud darling of old
nations whereamong she moved as a ruinous

flame, pre-figured the witch-woman. The apostrophe of Faustus to Queen Helen, apart from the mere loveliness of words, thus pulsates with an emotion for there is really no expression in human speech. In imagination the poet for one breathless moment, stands—as he perfectly believed, you must remember, that Johan Faustus had stood,—face to face with that flawless beauty of which all poets have perturbedly divined the existence somewhere, and which life as men know it simply does not afford, nor anywhere foresee. To Marlowe's mind, it was for this that Faustus pawned his soul, and drove no intolerable bargain: and the moral which Marlowe educes, wistfully, when all is over, is that a man must pay dearly for doing —not what heaven disapproves of, as would speed the orthodox tag,—but that which heaven nowadays does not permit. . . Of course his hero technically "repents", with a considerable display of rhetoric; but not until his lease of enjoyment is quite run out, and hell is pyrotechnically a-gape: by the prosaic the ethical value of "repentance" for the necessity of discharging an ardently unpleasant debt may be questioned. There is really no trace of regret for the hellish compact until punishment therefor impends: and then, by a stupendous touch of irony, Faustus is dragged to torment just as his parched lips pervert, to shriek his need, in terror-stricken babblement, that sugared and langorous verse which Ovid whispered in Corinna's arms, at the summit of life's felicity.

In short, this Christopher Marlowe was one of the supreme artists of literature. . .

5

We may lay finger upon this much, then, as increment, toward justifying Marlowe's economy. This much we have to set against its purchase price, which at crude utmost was the flung-away life of a shoe-maker's oldest son, very discreditably murdered at twenty-nine. All this, it must be remembered, was created —tangibly to exist where before existed nothing,—by a young fellow who, as went material things, was wasting his prospects in pot-house dissipation. At the birth of much of if not all this loveliness alcohol played the midwife. And really to make this admission need not trouble us, even nowadays when, at the moment I speak, we have so far advanced toward barbarism as to have adopted, with other doctrines of Islam, the tribal taboo, in the form of Prohibition; and are resolute to let art take its chances, with the other amenities of life, under that new régime, which so alluringly promises alike to outlaw the views of Christ concerning alcoholic beverages, and to enable zealous Christians to turn an honest penny by spy-work.

For, faithful in this as in all else to his abstention from logic, man has never believed his moral standards to be retro-active. We are so constituted that we can whole-heartedly detest from afar whatever our neighbors consider to be undesirable, when it is a measure of miles which removes the object of disapproval, but not when the thing is remote by a span of years. Of course in this there is no more display of reason than we evince, say, in the selection of our wives. In abstract theory, people ought to-day to view the infamy of Heliogabalus with at least the disfavor we reserve for our neighbors' children: in practise, a knave's wickedness becomes with time an element of romance, and large iniquities serve as colorful relief to the tedium of history. And it seems banal to point out that it no longer matters ethically, to anyone breathing, that a shoe-maker's son, rather more

102

than three centuries ago, made ruin of his body through intemperance, for the case is no longer within the jurisdiction of morals. Our sole concern with Marlowe nowadays is æsthetic: and the most strait-laced may permissibly commend the *Faustus* with much of that indifference to the author's personal "morality" which renders their enjoyment of the *Book of Psalms* immune to memories of the deplorable affair with Uriah's wife.

6

Then there is yet another versifier, François Villon, whose doings in the flesh allure me here toward a parenthetic and resistless illustration of what I have in mind: for, of course, among the many morals suggested out of hand by the terrestrial career of Villon the most perturbing is that depravity may, in the last quarter of every other blue moon, be positively praiseworthy. A many other notable poets have been deplorable citizens; hundreds of them have come to physical and spiritual ruin through drunkenness and debauchery: yet over these others, even over Marlowe if you be particularly obtuse, it is possible to pull a long face, in at any event the class-room, and to assume that their verses would have been infinitely better if only the misguided writers thereof had lived a trifle more decorously. But with Villon no such genteel evasion is permissible. The *Grand Testament* is a direct result of its author's having been, plus genius, a sneakthief, a pimp, and a cut-throat. From personal experience painfully attained in the practise of these several vocations it was that Villon wove imperishable verses, and he could not have come by this experience in any other way. So we have this Testament, which is an inseparable medley of sneers and beauty and grief and plain nastiness (and wherein each quality bewilderingly begets the other three), as the reaction of a certain personality to certain experiences. We are heartily glad to have this Testament: and upon the whole, we are grateful to Villon for having done whatever was necessary to produce these poems. And no sane person would contemn the Ballade au Nom de la Fortune, the Regrets de la Beale Heaulmière, and the Épitaphe, on the score that their purchase price was severally the necessity of forcing a man of genius to occupy a jail, a brothel and a gibbet. For again our moral prejudices fail to traverse the corridors of time;

and we really cannot bother at this late day to regain the viewpoint of the Capetian police.

Just here, moreover, the career of Villon suggests a subsidiary moral, as to the quaint and rather general human habit of "being practical." Villon stole purses, and the constabulary hunted him down, through "practical" motives: and it is salutary to reflect that both these facts are to-day of equal unimportance with all the other coeval manifestations of common-sense. Thus, for example, it was in Villon's generation that Jeanne Darc drove the English out of France, and Louis the Eleventh established the French monarchy in actual power,—both "practical" and, as it seemed, really important proceedings, of the sort to which marked prominence is accorded in the history-books. Yet the French monarchy to-day shares limbo with the court of Nimrod; dozens of English armies have entered France since the Maid's martyrdom in Rouen Square, and not always to the displeasure of Frenchmen: but the emotion with which a vagabond in 1461 regarded a loaf of bread in a bakery window survives unchanged. *Et pain ne voyent qu'aux fenestres,* he wrote: and his action in setting down that single line has proven a more lasting and a more momentous feat than the capture of Orléans. Then, when you consider all the "practical" persons of Villon's acquaintance,—the bishops and lords and princes, the lawyers and long-robed physicians, the merchants and grave magistrates and other citizens of unstained repute, who self-respectingly went about important duties, and discharged them with credit,—you cannot but marvel that of this vast and complicated polity, which took itself so seriously, nothing should have remained vital save the wail, as of a hurt child, that life should be so "horrid." For this is all that survives to us, all that stays really alive, of the France of Louis the Eleventh. . .

Presently I shall return to this fallacy of "being practical." Meanwhile, let it be repeated, Villon even when he jeers does but transmit to us the woe of an astounded and very dirty child that life should be so "horrid." He does not reason about it: here if anywhere was a great poet "delivered from thought, from the base holiness of intellect," and Villon reasons about nothing: but his grief is peculiarly acute, and in the outcome contagious. It is so cruel, he laments, that youth and vigor should be but transient loans, and that even I should have

become as bald as a peeled turnip; so cruel
that death should be waiting like a tipstaff to
hale each of us, even me, into the dark prison
of the grave; and so cruel that the troubling
beauty of great queens, and even the prettiness
of those adorable girls with whom I used to
frolic, should be so soon converted into a
wrinkled bag of bones. It is very cruel, too,
that because I borrowed a purseful of money
when the owner was looking elsewhere, I should
be locked in this uncomfortable dungeon; I had
to have some money. And it is perfectly preposterous that, merely because I lost my temper
and knifed a rascal, who was no conceivable
loss to anybody, the sheriff should be going to
hang me on a filthy gallows, where presently
the beak of a be-draggled crow will be pecking
at my face like the needle at my old mother's
thimble. For I never really meant any harm!
. . In short, to Villon's finding, life, not merely
as the parish authorities order it, but as the
laws of nature constrain it too, is so "horrid"
that the only way of rendering life endurable
is to drink as much wine as one can come by.
Besides, wine gives you such stupendous notions for a ballade, and enables you to comprehend the importance of writing it, as you,

who are so woefully unappreciated, who are so soon to die, alone can write it: and equally does wine sustain you through the slow fine toil of getting all the lovely words just right. . . There in little we have Villon's creed. It is not a particularly "uplifting" form of faith, save in the sense that it sometimes leads toward elevation at a rope's end: but Villon is sincere about it, poignantly sincere: and his very real terror and his bewilderment at the trap in which he was born, and his delight in all life's colorful things, that are doubly endeared by his keen sense of their impermanence, are unerringly communicated. . . Pity and terror: this —dare one repeat?—was what Aristotle demanded in great poetry: and this it is that Villon gives, full measure.

And we who receive the gift, all we who profit thus directly by the fact that François Villon was in the flesh, plus genius, a sneak-thief, a pimp, and a cut-throat—why, we may very well protest that our sole concern with the long-dead is æsthetic. For that is a more comfortable course than its alternative, which is to make confession that Villon's depravity has proven positively praiseworthy. Yet, either way, we have no right to dwell obtusely upon a circumstance which Villon himself is reported to have disposed of, once for all:— "When Paris had need of a singer Fate made the man. To kings' courts she lifted him; to thieves' hovels she thrust him down; and past Lutetia's palaces and abbeys and taverns and gutters and prisons and its very gallows—past each in turn the man was dragged, that he might make the Song of Paris. So the song was made: and as long as Paris endures François Villon will be remembered. Villon the singer Fate fashioned as was needful: and in this fashioning Villon the man was ruined in body and soul. And the song was worth it."

To-day of course nobody anywhere deliberates denying that the song was very well worth it. One may permissibly dispute what call there was to drag Fate into the business: but there is no possible disputing that Villon's first homicide was one of the luckiest accidents in the history of literature; and that a throng of ingrates have failed to render any appropriate gratitude to Dom Philippe Sermaise, for allowing himself to be killed so easily, by a novice in misdemeanor. . .

7

Our sole concern with the long dead (we are

thus driven to concede) is æsthetic: and it was æsthetically that Villon and Marlowe, in common with a host of confrères, have demonstrated their talent for economy. . . To a few of us it must always remain a source of intermittent regret that we have no medium of expression save the one human body which we to some extent, if only for a while, control. If you will quite rationally consider a looking-glass you will get food for illimitable wonder in the thought that the peering animal you find there, to all other persons, represents you: and probably there is nobody but has been shocked to identify one of those ambulatory reflections of queer people, in the mirror of a shop-window, as himself. That moving carcass does but very inadequately symbolize you, who, as a matter of open Sabbatical report, are a subtle and immortal spirit: nor does it afford any outlet to powers which you obscurely feel that you possess, and must perforce permit to come to nothing, like starved prisoners that perish slowly. . . The thing is rather a parody, in dubious taste. . . So far from being you, it is not even really under your control. Pre-figuring it as your residence, you are immured in the garret, where you have telephonic communication with the rest of the house. But a house remains quiescent: whereas this thing incredibly sprouts lawns of hair; concocts, as no chemist can do, its saliva and sweat and gastric juices, with a host of mysterious secretions, and uses them intelligently; makes and fits on a vitreous armor for the tips of its toes and fingers; builds up and glazes and renews its sentient teeth; despatches, to course about its arteries, innumerable rivulets of blood, with colonies of living creatures voyaging thereon; and of its own accord performs a hundred other monstrous activities in which you have no say. A third of the time, indeed, this commonwealth which you affect to rule takes holiday, willy-nilly, and you are stripped even of pretendership by sleep. Meanwhile the thing restlessly destroys and rebuilds itself. There is no particle of it, in the arms and legs or anywhere, which those hands before you have not lifted and put into the mouth's humid cavern: nor is there remaining to-day one atom of the body you frequented ten years ago. For incessantly it sloughs and renews and recasts itself, this apparently constant body: so that you are afforded neither a private nor a permanent residence, but wander about earth like a wind-whirl over a roadway, in a vortex of ever-changing dust.

And yet this body is likewise a cunning and elaborate piece of mechanism, over which you possess a deal of influence, for a limited while; and is an apparatus wherewith something might conceivably be done. And so, those covetous-minded persons, the creative writers—the poets, the *poietes*, the "makers"—endeavor with this loaned machinery to make something permanent.

Deluded people who view life sensibly—through the misleading reports transmitted to the brain-centres by man's gullible five senses, —aim otherwhither and gravely weave ropes of sand. It is they who, with a portentousness which laughter-loving cherubs no doubt appreciate, commend the "middle road". They live temperately, display edifying virtues, put money in bank, rise at need to heroism and abnegation, serve on committees, dispense a rational benevolence in which there is in reality something divine, discourse very wisely over flat-topped desks, and eventually die to the honest regret of their associates. And for such-an-one that forthwith begins to end his achievement here. No doubt the gates of heaven fly open, and his sturdy spirit sets about celestial labor: but upon earth he has got of his body no enduring increment. He has left nothing durable to signalize his stay upon this planet. Mementoes there may be in the shape of children: yet the days of these children also are numbered by no prodigal mathematician: and since to these children—who were created when his thoughts ran upon other matters,—he is certain to transmit his habits, they too in turn beget futilities. Meanwhile has the "practical" person builded a house, it is in time torn down, it burns, or else it crumbles: and his bungalow, or his paper-mill, or his free circulating library, fronts on the spires of Carthage and the Temple of Solomon. Has he contrived a beneficial law with Lycurgus, or a useful invention with Alfred the Great, his race in the progress of years outgrows employment of it. Has he created a civilization, it passes and is at one with Assyria and Babylon. Has he even founded a religion, the faith he evinced by martyrdom is taken over by an organized church, and pared down to the tenet that it is good form to agree with your neighbors. . . But the tale is old as to what befalls all human endeavors that are prompted by common-sense.

"Consider in thy mind, for example's sake, the times of Vespasian: consider now the times of Trajan: and in like manner consider all other periods, both of times and of whole nations, and see how many men, after they had with all their might and main intended and prosecuted some one worldly thing or other, did drop away and were resolved into the elements." And Marcus Aurelius was in the right of it: by making any orthodox use of your body and brain you can get out of them only ephemeral results. For all this code of common-sense, and this belief in the value of doing "practical" things, would seem to be but another dynamic illusion, through which romance retains the person of average intelligence in physical employment and, as a by-product, in an augmenting continuance of creature comforts. To every dupe, of course, romance assigns no more than a just adequate illusion; and squanders no unneeded cunning in contriving the deceit. So with men it is a truism that people of great mental powers are usually deficient in common-sense; for only the normally obtuse can be deluded by any pretence so tenuous as this of the ultimate value of doing "practical" things, and the acute waste time less self-deceivingly.

8

To some few of our multifarious race this
futile body-wasting practised by kings and
presidents and political parties, by ditch-
diggers and milliners and shrewd men of business, seems irrational. The thriftier artist is
resolved to get enduring increment of his body,
and by means of that movable carcass which
for a while he partially controls, to make something that may, with favoring luck, be permanent. Particularly does this incentive hearten
the craftsman in that creative literature wherethrough a man perpetuates his dreams. In all
other forms of chirographic exercise, wherein
the scribe expresses his knowledge and ostensible opinions,— as in history or in philosophy
or in love-letters or in novels that deal with
"vital" problems or in tax interrogatories,—
his writing is certain very soon to require re-
vision into conformity with altered conditions,
and is doomed ultimately to interest nobody.
In the sister arts, there needs only a glance
at the discolored canvases of Leonardo, or at
the battered Venus of the Louvre, to show that
here too time lies in wait to work disastrous
alchemy. But the dream once written down,

once snared with comely and fit words, may be perpetuated: its creator may usurp the brain-cells and prompt the flesh of generations born long after his own carnal loans are dust: and possibly he may do this—here is the lure—forever.

To authors who regard their art with actual reverence,—and beyond doubt exaggerate its possibilities as prodigally as their own,—this then is the creative writer's goal: it is to bring about this that he utilizes his human brain and body: and it is to this end he devotes those impermanencies. By any creative writer, as has been said, the human brain is perverted to uses for which it was perhaps not especially designed: nor is it certain that the human body was originally planned as a device for making marks on paper. Thus the serious artist, as well as the contributor to those justly popular magazines wherein the fiction is arranged, and to every appearance written, with a view of inducing people to read the advertisements, will very often damage his fleshly allotments in adapting them to serve his turn. And this would be a weighty consideration to the elect artist, who is above all else an economist, were

a man's brain or body, by any possibility of
hook or crook, and even in its present imper-
fection, to be retained by him. But these chat-
tels, as the elect artist alone would seem to comprehend, with any clarity, are but the loans of
time, who in an indeterminable while will have
need of his own. So always this problem con-
fronts the creative writer, as to what compromise is permissible between his existence
as an artist and his existence as an ephemeral
animal. And this problem has the dubious distinction of being absolutely the only question no
writer has ever settled, even to his own satisfaction. . .

Nor is this all. Enduring literature, as it is
necessary once more to point out in a land
where reviewers so incessantly dogmatize as
to this or that book's "truthfulness to life",
does not consist of reportorial work. It is not
a transcript of human speech and gesture, it
is not even "true to life" in any four-square
sense, nor are its materials to be drawn from
the level of our normal and trivial doings.
So that writers seldom establish their desks at
street-corners,—which would seem the obvious
course were it really anyone's business to copy
human life,—but to the contrary, affect libra-

ries, where they grumble over being disturbed by human intrusion. I shall presently come back to this vital falsity of "being true to life." . . Meanwhile the elect artist voluntarily purchases loneliness by a withdrawal from the plane of common life, since only in such isolation can he create. No doubt he takes with him his memories of things observed and things endured, which later may be utilized to lend plausibility and corroborative detail: but, precisely as in the *Book of Genesis,* here too the creator must begin *in vacuo.* And moreover, he must withdraw, for literary evaluation, to an attitude which is frankly abnormal. The viewpoint of "the man in the street" is really not the viewpoint of fine literature: their touchstones display very little more in common than is shared by the standards of lineal measure and avoirdupois weight: and for the greater part of every day, at meals, and in our family concerns, and in all relations with human beings, each one of us is perforce "the man in the street." It is thus from his own normal viewpoint that the artist must withdraw. . . And sometimes the mind goes of its own accord into this withdrawal, and reverie abstracts the creative writer from the ties and aspirations

of his existence as a tax-payer. Of the pleasure
he knows then one need not speak: but it is
a noble pleasure. And sometimes the mind
plays the refractory child, and clings pertina-
ciously to the belongings of workaday life: and
abstraction will not come unaided. Then it
would seem that this ruthlessly far-seeing economist induces such withdrawal by extraneous
means (as people loosely say) as a matter of
course, and by mere extension of the principle
on which he closes his library door. . . Of the
pleasure he knows then one need not speak:
but, then also, the pleasure is noble. For now
he is conscious of stupendous notions: he comprehends the importance of writing down these
notions as he alone can write them: and feeling
himself to be a god, with eternity held in fee, he
need not grudge the slow and comminuted labor
of getting all his lovely words just right. And
now he is for the while released from inhibitions
which compel him ordinarily to affect agree-
ment with the quaint irrationalities of "practical" persons. For in his sober senses, of
course, the economist dare not ever be entirely
himself, but must pretend to be, like everybody
else, admiringly respectful of bankers and
archbishops and brigadier-generals and presi-

dents, as the highliest developed forms of humanity. So it is from his own double-dealing that he induces a withdrawal; and with drugs or alcohol unlocks the cell wherein his cowardice ordinarily imprisons his actual self. Nor with him does there appear to be any question of self-sacrifice or self-injury, since, as he can perceive with unmerciful clearness, a man's brain and body are no more a part of him than is the brandy or the opium. All are extraneous things; and are implements of which the economist makes use to serve his end. So the abstraction is induced, the dream is captured: and presently, of course, this withdrawal requires augmented prompting. . . Thus the wind-whirl passes with heightened speed, and the dust it animated is quiet a little sooner than any inevitable need was. And subsequently commentators are put to the trouble of exposing "unsubstantiated traditions" and "calumnies of Griswold" and "Bacchic myths" and "symbolic vines", in annotated editions for the use of class-rooms.

9

For to some of us this economy seems wrong. There is no flaw in it perhaps, as a matter of pure reason: but reasoning very often conducts one to undesirable results, and after all has no claim to be considered infallible. . . Drugged by the fumes of moral indignation, we will even protest that, inasmuch as Professor Henry Wadsworth Longfellow was a man of irreproachable habits, and it was only yesterday that the Christian Disciples' pulpit was adorned by the Reverend Harold Bell Wright (to whom I shall recur for admiring consideration), it is, among other inferences, a self-evident proposition that Shakespeare did not die as the result of a drinking-bout. Conceivably the syllogism is not builded of perennial brass. But, as has been said, it seems at first sight, to every reputable connoisseur of art, that the only possible way to confront this unpleasant truth is to deny its existence. We somehow know, again led by instinctive wisdom, that it is more salutary for us to perceive in this mythos of the *Dive Bouteille*, which clings with annoying uniformity to so many great creative writers, simply a proof of their detractors' uninventiveness. . . For we admire our corner of the planet, we prize our span of life, and we cherish our bodies with a certain tenderness. It is not the part of a well-balanced person, say we, to think of such "economy", nor to appraise a man's relative importance in human life, far less in the material universe, after any such high-flown and morbid fashion, so long as there is the daily paper with all the local news. So we take refuge in that dynamic illusion known as common-sense; and wax sagacious over state elections and the children's progress at school and the misdemeanors of the cook, and other trivialities which accident places so near the eye that they seem large: and we care not a button that all about us flows and gyrates unceasingly an endless and inconceivable jumble of rotatory blazing gas and frozen spheres and detonating comets, wherethrough spins Earth like a frail midge. And we decline, very emphatically, to consider the universe as a whole—"to encounter Pan", as the old Greeks phrased it, who rumored that this thing sometimes befell a mortal, but asserted likewise that the man was afterward insane. They seem to have had the root of the matter.

10

Yet Pan is eternal and ubiquitous, whatever we might prefer to have him. . . So perhaps the creative writer will continue indefinitely to abuse and wreck that inadequate human body which is his sole medium of expression, in an endeavor to compel the thing to serve his desire. It may be, of course, that he also is sometimes led by instinctive wisdom, and achieves economy with no more forethought than bees devote to the blending of honey: even when the case stands thus, the fact is in no way altered that actually the creative writer, alone of mankind, does in a logical fashion attempt the unhuman virtue of economy. Whether consciously or no, he labors to perpetuate something of himself in the one sphere of which he is certain, and strives in the only way unbarred to create against the last reach of futurity that which was not anywhere before he made it. He breaks his implements with ruthless usage; he ruins all that time will loan: meanwhile the work goes forward, with fair promise. Yet a little while, as he assuredly reflects, and there will be no call for moral indignation, since it will be his book alone that will endure. And considering that wondrous volume, the archbishops and aldermen and pedagogues and leading philanthropists of oncoming years will concede that it was the reputed wastrel who played the usurer with his loaned body, and thriftily extorted interest, while those contemporaries who listened to the siren voice of common-sense were passing in limousines toward oblivion. . . So it is that the verbal artist and the "practical" person must always pity each other: and when it comes to deciding which is in reality the wastrel, there seems a great deal to be said for both sides.

Perhaps that is a moral of no large ethical value. But I am afraid there is nothing of the sort in the whole sorry business. Meanwhile you must remember that this cult of Art is very ancient, and began in days when goddesses were honored by human sacrifice. I think it is Thomas ā Kempis who reports that an old custom is not lightly broken.

V

THE REACTIONARY

—Have I the *air Francais?* . . . For you must know, 'tis as ill breeding now to speak good English as to write good English, good sense or a good hand. . . . But, Lord! that old people should be such fools! I wonder how old people can be fooled so! . . .

—The parson will expound it to you, cousin. . . .

—I knew there was a mistake in't somehow . . For the parson was mistaken, uncle, it seems, ha! ha! ha!

—The mistake will not be rectified now, nephew.

—The Gentleman Dancing Master

V

Which Considers the Reactionary

YET, if an old custom be not lightly broken in this cult of Art, it is equally a truism that therein all customs inevitably alter, and variability, here as elsewhere, attests the presence of vitality. . . . So it happens that, at the moment I speak, "the reign of the Puritan in literature" is the target of considerable not over-civil comment: and everywhere *les jeunes* are vociferously demanding their right to a candid and fearless exposition of life as it actually is. Alike in smashing and in splintered prose (which latter form they playfully list as *vers libre*), and via a pullulation of queer-looking little magazines, these earnest if rather quaint young people are expounding their "personal reactions". . . . For to obtrude some reference to "the reaction" seems now as much the badge of this movement as was in 1830 *enjambement* of a French Romanticist or in 1590 a far-fetched metaphor of an English Euphist. "Ah, yes, but just what, precisely, is

my reaction to this?'' is considered nowadays,
I am informed, the correct attitude toward art
and life alike, among all really earnest think-
ers. . . And the badge is happily chosen: for,
of course, this is but the latest form of that ageless reaction which is bred in every generation
by unavoidable perception that its parents have
muddled matters beyond human patience. Thus
the necessary incentive remains inveterate,
leaving merely the question what is to be done
about it all, for each generation to answer with
pleasing variousness.

So, it is well enough that ''earnestness''
should have its little hour along with the uke-
lele, just as a ''red-blooded reversion to primal
instincts'' coincided in its fleet vogue with
that other parlor-game called pingpong, and in
the remote era of progressive-euchre parties
pretty much everything was ''subtle'' and
''perverse'' and ''fiery-colored''. And really,
that a demand for liberty to talk on any and
all subjects should prove always a pleonasm
for limiting the discussion to sexual matters, is
proper enough, too, if only because it is the
natural business of young people to outdo their
elders, as touches both interest and performance, in such affairs.

128

In every seriously taken pursuit, of course, the influence of the Puritan augments daily: and the enaction of laws prohibiting anything from which light-minded persons might conceivably derive enjoyment remains our real national pastime. But it seems actually a general æsthetic movement, this ousting of the Puritan from control of our reading-matter: and since to the clear-seeing Puritan this reading-matter does not appear a potential source of pleasure to anybody, the movement has little opposition. If only the experiment had not been tried, over and over again, one might look forward to the outcome with an optimism less lukewarm. But the progress of romance I take to be a purely natural force: and in nature, as has been strikingly observed, any number of times, there are no straight lines. Art thus does not always go forward, but moves in recurrent cycles, as inevitably as the planets and tides and seasons, and all else which is natural. For "the continual slight novelty" recommended by Aristotle or some other old-fashioned person, is the demand of universal nature, and in consequence of art: so that, as you will remember, St. Paul very feelingly comments upon this craving as characteristic of the most

artistic people that ever lived, in his address
to the Athenians.

Thus it comes about, humiliating as may
seem the concession, that what is happening
to-day in America is really not in essentials
different from what happened in England as
far back as 1660. Then too "the reign of the
Puritan in literature" was triumphantly done
away with, once for all. . . And it is to this
quaint analogue that I must for a moment
divert, as illustrating very exactly what I have
in mind. . .

2

In England 1660 marked a rather wide adop-
tion, toward life in general, of that attitude
which, as distinguished from the Chivalrous
view, is describable as Gallantry. I have read
that the secret of Gallantry is to accept the
pleasures of life leisurely, and its inconveniences with a shrug; as well as that, among
other requisites, the gallant person will always
consider the world with a smile of toleration,
and his own doings with a smile of honest
amusement, and Heaven with a smile which is
not distrustful,—being thoroughly persuaded

130

that God is kindlier than the genteel would regard as rational.

In fine, the gallant person is a well-balanced sceptic, who comprehends that he knows very little, and probably amounts to somewhat less, but has the grace to keep his temper. This as a creed of conduct, of course, is ancient: you will find it illustrated certainly as far back as in the disreputable Jurgen legends of Poictesme, if indeed it was not explicitly voiced even earlier by Horace. And precisely as in the case of Chivalry, this too is a creed which still retains adherents; so that even here in Fairhaven my friends Robert Townsend and Rudolph Musgrave, to me at least, exemplify the Gallant and the Chivalrous types, as lingering survivals left at hopeless odds with an era unpropitious to either. . .

3

If one is indeed known by the company he keeps out of, Gallantry entered England very ill-recommended. Those dissolute and picturesque Cavaliers of the Restoration were really no fit companions for any self-respecting attitude toward life. They came swaggering into

England, swearing a many mouth-filling oaths, and chivied Mrs. Grundy, who was then no less much-thought-of for being not yet christened, up and down and out of the island, as a dowdy harridan. She has regained her own, *dei gratia,* since then: but, being feminine, she has never forgiven those who once decreed her out of fashion: and the schoolbooks she licenses will smugly inform you, any day, that this was the most "immoral" period in English history.

The description, like most of Mrs. Grundy's verdicts, is sufficiently sonorous to insure its repetition without the attachment of much particular meaning. Indeed, for all that the famed difficulties of getting a camel into a needle's eye are insignificant compared with the task of getting an era into a sentence, almost any book treating of the past is by ordinary a Museum of Unnatural History, wherein one views the bones of extinct epochs carefully wired into artificial coherency and ticketed with an authoritative-looking placard. Of all these labels none is better known than the adjective "immoral" attached to the period of the English Restoration. . . That, though, is because its "immorality" was itself a moral which men prefer not to face. One is told that this period

132

was indecent, and the information has a substratum of veracity. Yet 1660 is only the corollary of 1649: and England being once wedded to Puritanism, the union, after enduring ten years, was pretty sure to produce a Duchess of Cleveland at the helm of state, and a William Wycherley at the head of its literature. It was the human "reaction" to a decade of supernal thinking.

When the king had bravely stepped out of the window at Whitehall, a prohibitory tax was laid on mental cakes and ale. An epidemic of gloomy apprehensions in the guise of religion devastated the three kingdoms, and agreed one with another in the single tenet that since life is short you must even affairs by wearing a long face. Theological bickering succeeded the struggles of civil war: and unsatiated by Worcester and Marston Moor, dialecticians fought and refought Armageddon. The beneficent purpose of life—as a matter of public knowledge—was to afford all men a chance of escaping hell, by making earth equally unattractive. Vice went thriftily clad in fanaticism, for piety, or at least a vociferous impersonation thereof, was expected of everyone. . . It was one of those not infrequent historical instances when the rank and file of men have actually acquired a noble idea, and have gone mad under the unaccustomed stimulus,—such revolutions as have their modern analogue in the world-wide movement toward Prohibition, which, as I need hardly say, has resulted in unseemly excesses and a deplorable abuse of alcohol by our leading temperance workers. . . Never before or since has hypocrisy, even in England, received such disastrous encouragement. Children began life firmly impressed with the burden of original sin, and simultaneously assumed the responsibilities of Christianity and the first pinafore.

It has been plausibly suggested to have been through a not unnatural confusion that these children, with time's advancement, were prone to lay aside both together. No sooner is Cromwell buried than comes treading over his grave an uproarious train, rustling in satin, rippling with laughter, and extravagant in misdoing. It is the exiled "man Charles Stuart", returning at the head of a retinue of tailors, cooks and strumpets—of panders, priests, swashbucklers, perfumers, pickpockets, and an entire peerage,—yesterday's mendicants, to whom a kingdom has been given wherewith to amuse themselves. Ten years of beggary and vagabondage not being the best conceivable training for a monarch and his advisers, it is inevitable that they perform queer antics. England is topsy-turvy: sobriety is esteemed as quaintly out-of-fashion wear as the late Queen Elizabeth's ruff or the casque with which her predecessor affrighted the air of Agincourt. If any offences stay uncommitted against decorum, it is merely because no one has thought of them. Certainly, no person of quality ever remembers social restrictions save when considering how most piquantly to break them. . . Lord Buckhurst and Sir Charles Sedley, for example, gain prestige as humorists by appearing in the streets of London Adam-naked: 'tis conceded by the wits to be a vastly diverting jest, for Gallantry is yet in its boisterous youth. Where decorum had stalked unchecked for years, at last the revolution has set in, as against any other tyrant. The Restoration is thus far "immoral", but profoundly logical. As for condemning, there is always danger in hasty judgments: and investigation has ere now suggested that Nero was throughout the victim of his artistic temperament, and that the dog in the manger was a neurasthenic in search of rest and quiet. . .

Questionless, if the English of the day were somewhat lacking in hidebound morality, they seem to have trod the primrose way with honest enjoyment, and to have anticipated in the reputed bonfire just ahead, at the very worst, a *feu de joie*. Meanwhile the air they breathed was filled with animation, gayety, wit and excitement. For these people were guilty of enjoying existence without analyses, in a period of Externals, wherein hearts pumped blood and had no recognized avocations. Of a gentleman it was everywhere expected, as the requisites of social success, to make improper advances gracefully; and to dress not more than a month behind the Court of Fontainebleau; and to fence well enough to pink his man in an occasional duel back of Montague House; and to say resistlessly in French that which he ought not to say at all.

For conversation was now an art. You adopted it as a profession, and labored assiduously toward graduation as a wit. Persons of *ton* who properly valued their reputations would spend at least an hour in bed devising impromptus while the day was being aired.

They ornamented their language as carefully as their bodies: the sting of an epigram was as important as the set of a periwig: and the aspiring were at no little pains to crowd all their envy, hatred and uncharitableness into a perfectly phrased sentence, while wistfully hoping that its rounded and compact malignance might rouse approving laughter in the coffee-houses. . . For that was fame, albeit fame of a sort which is hardly appreciable nowadays, when thoughts are polished solely against potential appearance in a book. When two or three taxpayers are gathered together for the sake of what we humorously describe as conversation, it is salutary to remember that you may retain far better repute as touches sanity after discharging a shotgun into the midst of the group than will survive the loosing of a "rhetorical" sentence. But men were less partial to the slipshod on flambeaux-lighted Restoration evenings, when Killigrew and Rochester capped jests, and ornate paradoxes went boldly about tavern-tables, secure of applause, and with no weightier misgiving than the offchance of clashing with some more cleverly worded aspersion of human nature.

4

Such were the beaux who loitered through the parks by day, and at night, with congenial female companions, thronged the side-boxes of the theatres. They had assembled to be amused, and in 1660 nothing in dramatic form in England was able to bring about this consummation. There was only the Elizabethan and Jacobean drama, which was to them—as it remains to-day to the more honest of our contemporaries,—all very admirable, no doubt, in a remote high-minded sort of way, but without any possible doubt, deplorably old-fashioned. Such an audience puzzling over *Hamlet, Prince of Denmark,* as revived by the Duke's company, is a repetition of the ancient fable,— a group of splendid, shimmering and not at all erudite cocks gathered around a jewel, which they find curious but tasteless. Their "reaction", in fine, was plain boredom: and "the old plays," as Evelyn recorded after sitting through this *Hamlet,* "begin to disgust our refined age." This Shakespeare, about whom their fathers made such a to-do, had evidently been over-rated: his tragedies were lacking in correctness, and certainly were unlike those of

138

that newly discovered genius, in France yonder, Jean Racine: as for his comedies, they were insipid things compared with those which that really diverting rascal, Molière, was producing every week or two, in France, where King Lewis himself took part in them. Thus it was that to these people, too, came the unavoidable perception that their parents had muddled æsthetic matters beyond human patience.

So English audiences demanded new plays, which would resemble those French dramas that it was the very height of fashion to admire. They wished for something they could comprehend: like all uncultured persons, they were unable comfortably to venture in imagination beyond the orbits they traveled in flesh, and so preferred in art an exalted parody of their own everyday existence. They were bored by these mouthing thanes whose only assignations were with witches in a cave, and by these out-of-date Moors who smothered a faithless wife instead of allowing her a separate maintainance. They wished to see the stage bustling with people whose motives and doings they could understand and commend: so the beaux demanded heroines who, with delicious flutterings, stayed chaste pending the first procurable opportunity to be otherwise: and the fine ladies wanted as heroes flattered likenesses of last week's seducer, scented and irresistible, to parade triumphantly among the ruins of a shattered Decalogue.

The dramatists did their best toward compliance. A new style of comedy was improvised, which, for lack of a better term, we may agree to call the comedy of Gallantry, and which Etherege, and Shadwell, and Davenant, and Crowne, and Wycherley, and divers others, labored painstakingly to perfect. They probably exercised the full reach of their powers when they hammered into grossness their toofine witticisms just smuggled out of France, mixed them with additional breaches of decorum, and divided the result into five acts. For Gallantry, it must be repeated, was yet in its crude youth. . . So these comedies, however gaily received in those days, seem now a trifle depressing. Such uncensored philosophy may well have interested mankind when voiced by the lovely painted lips of Nell Gwynne or lisped by roguish Mrs. Knipp (Pepys' "merry jade"), when the beauty of the speaker loaned incisiveness to the phrase, and the waving of her fan could suggest naughtinesses. But now, in reading, the formal cadences of these elaborate improprieties blend, somehow, into a dirge, hollow and monotonous, over an era wherein undue importance would seem to have attached to concupiscence. The inhabitants can think of nothing else: continually they express the delusions of vice-commissioners and schoolboys in regard to the matter, and are bent upon having you believe that, behind the scenes, their amorous prowess puts to shame the house-fly. It is, if you insist, rather nasty: but, above all, it is so naïve. . . And at worse these "realists" did not pretend that their interest in such affairs,—an interest which is probably always more or less an obsession with the inexperienced,—had anything to do with altruism and the social reformation of humanity. It was merely to make sport they trifled with the quaintness of the still popular fallacy that human beings are monogamous animals, either by inclination or practise. For the comedy of Gallantry took its cue from the Court of Charles the Second, where morality was strictly conformable to the standards of spinsters whose inexplicable children were viewed with a peculiar tenderness by the king. And these Carolian arbiters—the Duchess of Cleveland, the Duchess of Portsmouth, the Duchess of Richmond, and other ladies of the bedchamber,—were not duchesses of Lewis Carroll's creation, intent on finding a moral in everything. . . One of these dainty iniquities had, indeed, bestowed considerable and even profoundly personal favors on Wycherley, in return for verses in praise of her ancient calling: and the dramatist, remembering it was the Duchess of Cleveland who had lifted him to fame and participation in royal privileges, felt perhaps that common gratitude demanded of him a little rough treatment of virtues any general practise of which would involve the destitution of his benefactress. Whatever his motives, Wycherley manifested scant respect for the integrity of the Seventh Commandment, or in fact for any sort of integrity. . .

5

This, of course, was very reprehensible. Yet the plays of this William Wycherley make rather more than interesting reading, for there is in his wit a genuine vigor that withstands the lapse of time and the distraction of explanatory notes. One may yet smile over the clever things said in his comedies, without being profoundly in sympathy with the speakers. For Wycherley's priapeans are, when you view them closely, in nothing an improvement upon actual human beings. They have forsaken blank verse for something very like the real speech of unusually quick-witted persons in social intercourse: and their behavior springs from no more exalted motives than people ordinarily bring into a drawing-room. In depicting character, and in his dialogue, Wycherley was the first of English writers to attempt anything like sustained "realism": and it is a quaint reflection that Jane Austen is his literary granddaughter.

It would be pleasant to discuss a little more amply this William Wycherley. The spendthrift had virile genius, which, had he chosen, might have made his name one of the greatest in English literature. Instead, he preferred to enjoy the material things of life, and, in the end, got from his endeavor to do so, very small comfort. . . But the man's work remains, for anybody to inspect at will: and all that is necessary to say as to the man himself has been, rather indulgently, set forth elsewhere.

So in his first youth he wrote four comedies,

in a manner that will always delight the judicious, because the desire to write perfectly was inborn in him: but all the while he was rather ashamed of his employment. To be classed with such queer cattle as authors, and be considered at the mercy of persons whom lack of any especial ability has reduced to writing criticisms for the newspapers, a little marred his renown as a leader of fashion, and indeed is still humiliating. Then many writers besides Wycherley have sometimes felt dejectedly that scribbling on paper is trivial employment for an adult. . . So he protests to his admirers, yawning carelessly behind his long white fingers, that these *jeux d'esprit* were written for his own amusement; mere trifles, in faith, scrawled at odd moments in his boyhood, and hastily strung together; nothing more, good hearts, he assures them. And his hearers, duly impressed, applaud this gentlemanly rogue, who has without any effort depicted vividly that which they understand and admire. For the age, like every other age as a whole, is not really interested in the mysteries of existence that move in orbits other than the round of daily life. Poetry, religion, high passion and clear thinking even now with most of us remain the x's and y's of a purely academic equation, and as unknown quantities, are as dubiously regarded in literature as elsewhere. But that which is "true to life" anyone of us can at once recognize, with a pleasant glow over his own cleverness.

6

Now it is unnecessary to enumerate all the points of resemblance between what may be euphemistically described as the present state of reading-matter in America and the very real literary art of the English Restoration. Nor is it needful to explain that, where these "realists" attempted to be as lively as their French models, our own "realists" are more ambitiously endeavoring to be at once as "daring" and as dull as the Russians. . . The main point is that in both cases the reaction was inevitable and not especially significant. The similarity next in importance is found by observing that these Restoration dramatists were the first English writers to fall into that dangerous and thrice dangerous practise with which our literature is threatened to-day, of allowing their art to be seriously influenced by the life about them.

For Wycherley and his confrères were the first Englishmen to depict mankind as leading an existence with no moral outcome. It was their sorry distinction to be the first of English authors to present a world of unscrupulous persons who entertained no especial prejudices, one way or the other, as touched ethical matters; to represent such persons as being attractive in their characteristics; and to represent such persons, not merely as going unpunished, but as thriving in all things. There was really never a more disastrous example of literature's stooping to copy life.

For of course the Restoration dramatists were misled by facts. They observed that in reality unscrupulous persons were very agreeable and likable companions; that the prizes of life fell to these unscrupulous persons; and that it is only the unscrupulous person who can retain always the blessing of an untroubled conscience. Anyone of us can to-day observe that such is still, and perhaps will be forever, the case in human society. And equally, everyone of us knows that in enduring literature of the first class this fact has always been ignored, and retributive justice, in the form of both gnawing remorse and physical misfortune, has with gratifying regularity requited the evil-doer.

7

Most great creative writers, in the pursuit of their emblematic art, have tended to present man's nature as being compounded of "good" and "evil" qualities,—presenting humanity in the explicit black and white of full-dress morality, as it were, without much intrusion of the intermediate shades of ordinary business-wear. And all great creative writers have as a rule rewarded the virtuous, but they have punished the wicked invariably. Here we touch on what is perhaps the most important illusion that romance fosters in man.

It can hardly be questioned that "good" and "evil" are æsthetic conventions, of romantic origin. The most of us, indeed, at various removes, quite candidly derive our standards in such matters from romantic art, as evinced in that anthology of poems and apologues and legends and pastorals and historical romances known collectively as the Bible. And therein, you will recall, the Saviour of mankind is represented as conveying his message by making up short stories in the form of parables, romance thus being very tremendously indicated as the true demiurge. . . But of the Bible I will speak later.

And were there nothing else to indicate the artistic origin of "good" and "evil", no one could fail to note that "goodness" everywhere takes the form of refraining from certain deeds. Every system of ethics, and every religion, has expressed its requirements in the form, not of ordering people to do so-and-so, but of "Thou shalt not do this or that". Thus the "wicked" have always retained a monopoly of terrestrial dealings, since the "good" have largely confined themselves to abstention therefrom. There is only one class of men conceivable to whom avoidance of action could figure as being in any circumstances praiseworthy: and that, of course, is the artist class, which alone can make use of, and indeed has need of, physical inactivity, wherein to evolve and perfect and embody its imaginings. To rational persons it is at once apparent that mere abstention from enormities cannot in itself constitute any very striking merit; and that rigorously keeping all the Ten Commandments, say, cannot possibly entitle you to supernal favoritism. You really cannot in reason ask, from either celestial or civic authorities, a reward for not being a thief or an adulterer, and expect to enter into eternal bliss on the ground of having kept out of jail. . . To the contrary, all religious precepts, when closely considered, can have no bearing whatever on any future life, and would seem to be the purely utilitarian figments of romance, as variously contrived with a view of improving the coherency and comeliness of life here.

Thus virtue has always been conceived of as victorious resistance to one's vital desire to do this, that or the other, and in a word as daily abstention from being "true to life". And that such abstinence will ultimately be rewarded full measure, is the lure which religion has always dangled before man,—very plainly in the demiurgic effort to exalt the animal, and to woo him away from "realism". . . So he moils forward, guided by the marsh-fire glitter of that other venerable artistic convention "the happy ending". For being "good" he will be paid, here in all probability, but certainly in a transfigured life to come. It is that dynamic belief which men generally entitle the sustaining force of religion. . . And religion, like all the other products of romance, is true in a far higher sense than are the unstable conditions of our physical life. Indeed, the most prosaic of materialists proclaim that we are all descended from an insane fish, who somehow evolved the idea that it was his duty to live on land, and eventually suceeded in doing it. So that now his earth-treading progeny manifest the same illogical aspiration toward heaven, their bankruptcy in common-sense may, even by material standards, have much the same incredible result.

8

Still, it is a pity we no longer really notice that material world which we unthinkingly contemn. Much abominable talk about "the unwholesome restlessness of modern life" is thus bred by our blindness to the fact that restlessness is pre-eminently a natural trait. All nature is restless, as men must very anciently have noted with troubled surmise, when they observed this constant and inexplicable moving of things. . . The world they inhabited was a place ineffably different from the planet which we utilize as a foundation for office-buildings, but then too the world was full of obvious unrest. For over their heads by day moved a

ball of fire, and at night a spotted plate, or
perhaps a crescent, of silver, moving among
innumerable lamps that guttered and sparkled
as they too moved, each as if of its own accord.
Incomprehensible objects, much like enormous
fleeces, likewise moved overhead by day, and
moved earthward at evening, to be dipped in
blood and dyed with gold. Sometimes would
come the moving pelts of more sombre mon-
sters, bellowing with rage, and these shaggy
horrors would fight one another with terrible
javelins, while the world wept and the frenzied
trees wailed aloud. Very often after such a
battle a triumphal arch, of all blended colors,
would arise as if of its own accord, in honor
of the victor. . . And on earth plants crept
out of the soil much as did the worms, and the
grass thrust through like little green swords,
always moving. Bushes and trees, that fastidi-
ously cast by and renewed their raiment, and
insanely relinquished it altogether when the
world was chilliest, were never still, but
moved always, and whispered secrets to one
another. Water wandered about earth, and
chattered and laughed as it moved. The very
fire in your cave moved too, as though struggling to free itself from the hearth, and if you

came within reach, it venomously stung you. . .
Men long ago noted this interminable restlessness, this unceasing movement, of insensate
things; and deduced, quite naturally, that invisible beings must exist who manipulated
them. Whether the deduction were right or
wrong, the approach to it was purely a matter
of reasoning: and man's interpretation of the
universe, through considering things as they
were, was in the terms of "realism". Men saw
the universe as the uncanny place that it remains to honest inspection. . .

9

Then appeared, as invariably appears, the
liberating reactionary. For romance, the first
and loveliest daughter of human vanity, took
charge of this interpretation, and transmuted
it, by whispering that these unseen beings were
vitally interested in mankind and in all the
doings of mankind. This, as I need hardly
point out, had nothing to do with reasoning: it
was not (upon the whole) a logical inference
based on the analogue of man's deep interest
in, say, the morals of gnats and lizards; but
was throughout the splendid and far-reaching
inspiration of romance. For now the demiurgic

spirit of romance revealed these beings, who had gifts to bestow, and led men thriftly to worship them. So that, by the grace of romance, the quite incredible "reaction" of man to all the mystery and vastness of the universe was a high-hearted faith alike in many impendent blessings and in his own importance.

For it was romance, the first and loveliest daughter of human vanity, that now caused religion to become dynamic, by presenting it as profitable to men. Straightway in Egypt hawk-headed Ra went forth, a divine philanthropist, to fight with the strong dragon Apap for man's welfare: and Queen Isis, crowned with the young moon, and attended by geese and serpents, set out upon her wanderings, burying here and there a fragment of her loved husband's body, so that men might get plentiful crops from the earth she thus made fertile. From Nineveh came Ishtah, in a chariot drawn by innumerable doves: she bore in one hand a cone-shaped pebble, and in the other a comb: thus she came mystically to reign as Mylitta in Babylon, as Astarte in Syria, as Tanith in Carthage, as Ashtaroth in Canaan, as Anaïtis in Armenia, and as Freia in the northlands, and everywhere to delight and madden mankind

with careful perversities of passion. About
India roamed Pushan, with his hair braided
spirally like a shell, and he carried a golden
spear wherewith to protect men from every ill:
and dreadful but not unpropitiable Kali, the
Contriver of Human Sorrows—the Black Goddess, whose joy was in curious torture,—might
sometimes be encountered there, in the form
of a tigress, intent to work evil among men.
And Olympos arose, in very much the fashion
of Ilium's fabled erection, to a noise of multitudinous music, and so revealed its passionate
and calm-eyed hierarchy: nymphs went about
the woods, so that in every coppice was the flash
of their silvery nakedness, and from stilled
forest pools came the green-haired Naiads: and
of all these romance consummated the nuptials,
at one time or another, with some member of
the human race, save only—by a fine truthful
touch—the Goddess of Wisdom. And north-
ward Thor smote terribly with his Hammer,
bringing the nourishing rain to men's tilled
places, and Balder the Ever-Beautiful, whom
blind Hoder slew unwittingly with a javelin of
mistletoe-wood, went down into Hela's cheerless habitation, there to abide until the gather-
ing of Ragnarok; so that virtuous persons

154

might then pass through the world's twilight, over the bright rainbow bridge, to revel eternally in Gimli, that paradise which the Æsir had builded for wise and valiant men. Everywhere, as romance evolved the colorful myths of religion, the main concern of the gods was, less with their own affairs, than with the doings of men: everywhere religion was directly profitable to men: and everywhere romance loaned to this new form of expression that peculiar beauty—which is delicate and strange, yet in large part thrills the observer by reason of its unexpected aptness,—such as always stamps the authentic work of romance.

10

Then the demiurge set about a masterpiece, and Christianity was revealed to men. . . There is really no product of romance more delightful than the Bible: but we are prone to appraise it, like everything else, from irrelevant standpoints. Thus we consider the Book piecemeal: we think of Abraham and Moses and David and Isaiah and Paul and Peter and so on, as individuals, and attempt, with something very like æsthetic sacrilege, to educe "lessons" from their several lives. To do this

is beyond any reasonable doubt a futile proceeding, and is to misapprehend the Author's
scale. For the proportion of any one of these
people to the story is not, as elsewhere, the
relation of a character to the tale in which it
figures, but rather the value of a word, or at
most a sentence, that is employed in narrating
the romance. In this great love-story there are
only the two characters of God and Humanity.
The men and women used as arbitrary symbols
in themselves signify very little. But viewed
collectively, like so many letters on a printed
page, they reveal a meaning, and it is
gigantic. . .

For I spoke just now of the Cinderella
legend, with its teaching of the inevitable very
public triumph of the neglected and downtrodden, as being the masterwork of romance.
Can you not see that the story of Christ, the
climax toward which the whole Bible-romance
moves as its dénouement, is but the story of
Cinderella set forth in more impressive terms?
—for therein the most neglected and downtrodden of humanity is revealed, not as a tin-
seled princess, but as the Creator and Master
of all things: and His very public triumph is
celebrated among the acclamation, not of any

human grandees and earls and lackeys, but of
the radiant hosts of Heaven. And you must
note the scale of this greater version! For as
the disregard and contumely accorded God is
dated from the Genesis of humanity, from the
primal beginnings of life, so is the ultimate
very public triumph celebrated amid the unim-
aginable pomp and fanfare of the vision seen
from Patmos. And then the firmament is rolled
up like a scroll that has been read to the end,
and the last type of life is removed from earth,
precisely as all type is removed from a "form"
after the manufacture of a very beautiful book
that is not intended as an article of commerce,
but is printed solely for the Author's
pleasure. . .

I spoke of Christianity as a product of romance. . . I have discoursed to little purpose
if that sounded to you like a slur upon Christianity: for from the beginning I have been contending that nothing in the universe is of importance, or is authentic to any serious sense,
except the various illusions of romance, the
demiurge. And I am frank to confess that I
elect to believe every word of the Bible. Indeed, to discover anything incredible therein
necessitates a rather highly developed form of

opththalmia in regard to what is miraculous.
It is possible only to those persons who somehow overlook the fact that they themselves are
miracles of dullness entirely surrounded by
miracles of romance. We should avoid such
beings. Personally, I find no difficulty in believing, for example, that Jonah was kept alive
for three days in the commodious interior of
a great fish, when I consider that I myself have
been kept alive for a number of years imprisoned in three pounds of fibrous matter here
in my skull. That Adam was modeled of clay,
and an immortal spirit breathed thereinto, is in
every way a more comprehensible and neat proceeding than that the physical union of two human bodies—a process in which the soul would
seem very certainly to take no part whatever,—
should not infrequently produce an infant who
is an immortal spirit. And finally, that Christ
turned water into wine, of noticeably superior
and heady quality, and gave it to His friends
to drink, is at the worst as consistent with
reason as that His most vociferous servitors
should demand to have any imitation of His
example rewarded with a jail-sentence. . . Ah,
no, there is no difficulty in the miracles and inconsistencies of the Bible, for us who live

among, and are made what we are, by miracles and inconsistencies.

Thus I am frank to confess that I elect to believe every word of the Bible. Its historical portions, I am told, have been shown to be untrue, but that is surely a very inadequate reason for exchanging belief in them for credence of the artless "facts" which "scholars" propose as substitutes. For as I have previously pointed out, our sole concern with the long-dead is æsthetic. Now æsthetically it makes for tedium to enthrone any such dull figure as the "historical" Pilgrim-Father-sounding Nebo-defend-the-crown in place of the picturesque potentate who ate grass like an ox, and certainly it makes for dryness to revise the world-engulfing Flood into a local freshet; whereas the Christ legend should always be believed in, without relation to the "realism" of inscriptions and codexes, because of the legend's beauty and usefulness to art. . . But suppose these things never happened? Why, but do you not see that to suppose anything of the sort is insane extravagance?—for it is to barter a lovely idea for a colorless one. No, whether the Bible-story be "historical" or not, the story is priceless either way, as a triumph of romantic art, in its apotheosis of the Cinderella legend.

So I spoke of Christianity as a product of romance, and as the masterpiece of romance. And such it veritably is: for if scribes who were not "divinely inspired" concocted and arranged the Bible as we have it, the Bible is past doubt the boldest and most splendid example of pure romance contrived by human ingenuity. But if it all really happened,—if one great Author did in point of fact shape the tale thus, employing men and women in the place of printed words,—it very overwhelmingly proves that our world is swayed by a Romancer of incalculable skill and imagination. And that the truth is this, precisely, is—again precisely,— what I have been contending from the start.

VI
THE CANDLE

—Mr. Scandal, for Heaven's sake, sir, try if you can dissuade him from turning poet.

—Poet! . . . Why, what the devil! has not your poverty made you enemies enough? must you needs show your wit to get more?

—Ay, more indeed: for who cares for anybody that has more wit than himself?

—Jeremy speaks like an oracle. . . . No, turn pimp, flatterer, quack, lawyer, parson, be chaplain to an atheist, or stallion to an old woman, anything but poet; for a poet is worse, more servile, timorous and fawning, than any I have named.

—*Love for Love*

VI

Which Values the Candle

WE have come a long way, from the petty villains of Wycherley to the eternal verities of religion. . . And in progress we seem to have deserted the Gallant attitude toward life, at a period when among English-speaking peoples this school of philosophy was yet in its boisterous youth. It matured, as I need hardly say, into something infinitely more urbane; and developed, as does every inspiration of the demiurge, in a direction very largely determined by the material this artist had just then in hand. Precisely as the sculptor's inspiration must conform to his supply of marble, so must romance be trammeled by working in the rarer and more stubborn medium of human intelligence.

Indeed, it is pitiable to observe how the most felicitous notions of the demiurge, when brought forcibly into contact with our general blockheadedness, fly off a tangent. Thus, for instance, it has long fared with Christianity, which I made bold to eulogize a moment ago as the supreme masterpiece of romance, however many well-meaning persons stand, to-day as always, ready to assure you that we have been very dismally privileged to witness "the world-wide failure of Christianity." Well, that is another verdict which will be settled by posterity, without, it is just conceivable, any prolonged consideration of my opinion. Meanwhile it is true that those few of us who believe that the principles of Christianity may perhaps some day be regarded seriously as rules of conduct are apt every once in a while to be staggered. A war, for example, may seem, to persons judging hastily, to render any such opinion untenable. Yet, when rightly viewed, the war-madness which is occasionally kindled to ravage Christendom, discredits nothing except the harmless pretensions of us church-members to be otherwise than academically interested in Christianity. The verity and beauty and the importance of Christianity remain unaffected, alike by the doings of laymen and clergy.

For of course the time-hallowed verdict of the clergy, when confronted by this mania, has been perfectly voiced by an honored and influential prelate: "All God's teachings about forgiveness should be rescinded for the enemy. I am willing to forgive our enemies for their atrocities just as soon as they are all shot. If you would give me happiness, just give me the sight of the leaders of the enemy hanging by the rope. If we forgive our enemies after the war, I shall think the whole universe has gone wrong."

Now that is pithily put: it leaves you in no manner of doubt as to the speaker's opinion of romantic Galilean doctrines, and candor is always worthy of commendation. And the clergy in every era have merited the praise due to this fearless stand. History must always record that in war-time the ministers of Christ, in every land and epoch, have bravely confessed that to their minds the exhortation to love your neighbor was in no way inconsistent with military endeavor to remove him from the face of the earth; and that to their minds the text concerning the blessedness of peacemakers should be "rescinded for the enemy." The clergy act bravely, be it repeated, for considerable courage is required to make public confession that your mind works in this fashion.

Nor for near twenty centuries have they once faltered in contending that the Sixth Commandment should be interpreted in a super-Pickwickian sense, since if only you were careful to commit your homicides wholesale and in the right uniform, manslaughter was an eminently praiseworthy pursuit. Any killing done in the wrong uniform, of course, is counted as another brutal atrocity: that has always been frankly conceded by the clergy, upon both sides. . . For everywhere in war-time the clergy are thrust into the delicate position of having to explain away explicit requirements with which their parishioners do not intend to be bothered just now: so that the clergy labor under what must be the very unpleasant obligation of talking truculent nonsense Sunday after Sunday, and of issuing a formal invitation to Omnipotence to take part in the carnage. However, the considerate person will always remember that rectors and bishops really have no alternative, short of falling out with their congregations: and that a clergyman who took the ground that Christ meant literally every word He said would get himself into very serious trouble. Meanwhile it is consoling to note that through every war the potential importance of Christianity, even as a possible standard of conduct, is re-suggested, by the fact that each revolt from Christian tenets, however enthusiastically abetted by all the vestries and diaconates, results in misery everywhere. And meanwhile, one more dynamic illusion of romance—the masterpiece of romance, in fact,—is temporarily baffled by coming into contact with human dunderheadedness, very much after the fashion in which, as was just pointed out, our man-made social orderings often bring to nothing the illusion known as love. For there is no denying that romance is flouted when churchmen "face the facts" (as sturdy capitalists put it) in a well-meant effort to patch up some superficial consistency between what the congregation is going to do at all hazards and the plaguily explicit teachings of an unparochial Saviour . . .

And the naive blasphemy of this is far worse than "wicked," because it is an abandonment of æsthetic principles. For this—do you not see?—is "realism": and, as I hasten to add, such "realism" as was hardly avoidable, by human nature. Since Constantine killed off all serious opposition to Christianity (in the literal fashion of an unimaginative soldier), and made Christianity upon the whole the most convenient religion for civilized persons to profess, the Christian church has been in war-time more or less driven to precisely that "realism" which was denounced by Sophocles. For an endowed and generally prosperous church cannot but sooner or later be seduced into regarding the men composing the average congregation as they are, instead of considering what men "ought to be," and holding them to that standard by the romantic and infallible process of assuming, as a matter of course, that it is a standard from which nobody ever deviates.

Unquestionably, "realism" is not upon a plane with arson or adultery, and so cannot be much palliated by circumstances. And it has even been suggested that in war-time some of the clergy, here and there, really believe what they preach. For the undeniable possibility of the case being such, however, we pew-holders are more to blame than the pastors, if only because the contemptuous indulgence everywhere accorded the clergy, as a sort of third sex, so shuts them off from normal life that many of them may well come quite honestly to confound the chief ends of human existence with church affairs. Now war has always

promoted "business," by the simple process of creating a need for that which
war destroyed. War has always thus directly
benefited that staid and undraftable class of
"business" men who compose vestries. Viewed
from the cloistered and necessarily somewhat
unsophisticated standpoint of most clergymen,
it must seem self-evidently not possible that
religion was intended to interfere with the continuance in well-doing of a leading vestryman
—no less esteemed as a personal friend than as
a parishioner of famed integrity and benevolence,—whose annual contribution to Foreign
Missions, and even to the Contingent Fund, is
dependent upon the state of his ledgers. That
the "business" of such a person is divinely provided, and made prosperous, it would be im-
pious to doubt. For, through everybody acting
conscientiously, all around, the clergy in many
instances come really to believe (in common
with their congregations) that church-work
comprises that attitude toward life which is
Christianity. They come, in short, to mistake
for the light of the world the candle that illu-
minates the altar. And thus it is very often
without any conscious and intelligent time-serv-
ing, no doubt, that prelates so intrepidly expose

to detestation that lack of self-restraint which they deplore when manifested on the battle-field, by reproducing it in the pulpit. . .

Thus it has been for some twenty centuries, and the end is not yet. Meanwhile the considerate person here and there to be born among oncoming generations will reflect that this very human hysteria under bell-towers in no way affected the authentic sun; and will insist that Christianity has been not at all "discredited," but remains the happiest effort of romance.

I have divagated at such length, as to this particular instance of the way in which the demiurge is occasionally foiled by human shortcomings, in part because it illustrates my thesis, with vivid pigments; and partly because, as I too become an old fogy, I turn with renewed tenderness to all else that grows obsolete, and so am inclined to defend the church, even in this matter, to the utmost effort of my out-of-date prejudices.

And much as what we so long nicknamed Christianity surrendered to material conditions, so did that other pleasing product of romance, which I have termed Gallantry, in due season compromise with material conditions,

170

though in a fashion, as I am happy to report, far less disastrous.

2

For the fun of shouting out the gross names of things is not inexhaustible. We have glanced at the dramatic literature of Gallantry as it was in the exuberance of youth, and we have noted its painstaking improprieties. . . Well, when the scented exquisites of Charles the Second's generation, a little the worse for the wear and tear of time, and a trifle shaken by the turmoil and uproar of 1688, crept out of the retirement into which the Revolution had thrust them, to lounge again on the shady side of the Mall, their juniors were beginning to wonder if this interminable obligation to be salacious had not reached the point of becoming tiresome. In large part this was the inevitable rebellion of a new generation against the existent order, whatever that may happen to be, in demanding "the continual slight novelty." Yet the reaction, as always, was given its general trend by material circumstances: for the all-powerful Whigs had of late displayed such turpitude that it was eminently necessary to emphasize their pious motives in everything. Thus, when people uncivilly pointed out that King William was an unhanged thief, his adherents could draw attention to his regular attendance at morning prayers: and when the Tories denounced Queen Mary as a parricide, Whigs could complacently counter with the equally undeniable facts that she did beautiful needlework and was particularly gracious to archbishops. Many of the less exigent virtues thus became quite modish.

The stage of course reflected this. So, after an existence of thirty years, the new comedy passed into a second period, like a married rake, vastly ameliorated in conduct, and not at all in morals. Toward the end of the seventeenth century it was still the fashion to speak encomiums of "manly Wycherley," whose piteous wrecked body as yet survived his intellect: but it was "the great Mr. Congreve" whose plays drew crowded houses.

For, beyond question, Mr. Congreve of the Middle Temple was the day's foremost writer. Such was the general opinion of his contemporaries, and it does not appear to have been bitterly disputed by Congreve. He is "the great Mr. Congreve," who, very much as Wycherley had done before Fleet Prison

eclipsed his genius, leads fashion as well as
literature: to honor Mr. Congreve critics contend in adulation, and even the pen of misan-
thropic John Dennis flows as with milk and
honey; whereas 'tis notorious that no woman
can resist Mr. Congreve's blandishments, from
Anne Bracegirdle the famous actress, to Henri-
etta Churchill, the equally famous Duchess of
Marlborough. He is "the great Mr. Congreve": and Mr. Dryden (the late laureate, and
himself a poet of considerable parts) doth not
hesitate to predict that the name of Congreve
will survive as long to posterity as the name
of Shakespeare. But, for that matter, so long
equally will live the names of Iscariot and
Simple Simon: and while it is well enough to
leave footprints on the sands of time, it is even
more important to make sure they point in a
commendable direction. . .

3

In his youth this William Congreve wrote
four comedies that will always delight the judicious, because in Congreve too was inborn the
desire to write perfectly of beautiful happenings These comedies I take to be the full and
well-nigh perfect expression of the Gallant atti-

tude. There has been no lack of persons to arraign them as "immoral" productions, and to point out that their sprightly dialogue is not with any painstaking exactitude modeled after the questions and answers of the Shorter Catechism. But really that sort of carping is rather silly. Congreve was writing for a definite audience—an assemblage of gallant persons,— and must give them what they would accept. The far less lucky Marlowe, as I have just indicated, was forced to write those "comic" scenes which make the blood of his admirers grill with shame, because his audience demanded that sort of thing: and dramatists have always labored under such necessities, very probably before Phrynichus suffered for reminding the Athenians of unpleasant topics, and quite certainly ever since Shakespeare stooped to vilify the Maid of Domrémy. Congreve's auditors had shown what subjects they considered suitable for comic treatment: and Wycherley had so far justified their belief as to demonstrate that from the materials they had chosen could be constructed excellent entertainment. If Congreve was to write for the stage, he must abide by its traditions as to the comedy of Gallantry. . .

As for the "grossness" of Congreve's
language, decorum in speech is largely a matter of chronology. The gallant pleasantries
of Congreve neither corrupted nor embar-
rassed his contemporaries. It was what they
were used to in daily life, with the difference
that the Congrevean version was more delicately worded: for anecdotes which even an
apple-cheeked boy in the company of his fellows might hesitate to repeat, were then narrated by divines from the pulpit. . . . Congreve
in short, has worn the mode of his day, and
permitted his art to be seriously influenced by
the life about him. As I have previously
pointed out, this is always a dangerous proceeding: and here we find a droll by-product of
such rash dalliance with "realism",—of depicting men more or less as they are,—in the
fact that with altered fashions the plays of
Congreve, which were formerly considered
models of elegance, have become "indecent"
reading. The lesson should be salutary. . .
Meanwhile we ought to be rational, and concede to an acknowledged leader of society the
right to wear the style of his day, in all things,
and to be *à la mode* alike in dress and speech.
Neither his language nor his periwig is just

at present in vogue: and that is the worst which can be said of either with justice. For really, should you fall to the rare practise of thinking, whether you allude to the strange woman as a "social problem" or plump out with a briefer Biblical synonym, the meaning conveyed is very much the same.

There remains, of course, the question of Congreve's ethical attitude. Toward the misdoings of which he treats, as innumerable moralists have lamented, his tone is one of amused acquiescence. Well, after all, that is a Gallant requisite—to "consider the world with a smile of toleration,"—and such remains the Gallant viewpoint even nowadays, however infrequently it is displayed in electrotype: Wycherley, as I have said, had perfidiously set forth the fact that Nemesis is by no means an infallible accountant: and Congreve, too, conceded this, though with more urbanity. For where the cynicism of Wycherley is exhibited in an onslaught, that of Congreve takes shape as a shrug. Wycherley, like most of us, was uncomfortable when people talked exaltedly outside of pulpits, and being free of obligations we labor under of pretending to like it, expressed his annoyance forcibly. But Congreve brushed aside such verbiage, and declined to make a pother over catchwords. Meanwhile he looked about him, and was convinced that men were not immaculate creatures: and his view of women's natural talent for chastity became such as nowadays only a very gifted woman dare express. . .

So Congreve makes no effort toward elevating or instructing his audience, despite his cool assertion that in each of his comedies is hidden a fable. "I designed the moral first, and to that moral I invented the fable," you will find the unconscionable fellow writing; and if this be so, the disguise of the apologue is remarkably efficient. For unquestionably none save Congreve ever accused his plots of being builded to point a moral. In fact, the unprejudiced would hardly have suspected his comedies of being constructed at all, for they have throughout the formless incoherence of ordinary human existence, and resemble actual life also in that the insignificance of what is being done is painstakingly veiled with much speaking. At the final curtain, you have no idea of the story: in memory lingers at most a glittering confusion of persons hiding in closets, juggling with important documents, inconse-

quently soliloquizing over their private affairs
for the benefit of eavesdroppers, and casually
marrying masked strangers. You recall,
clearly enough, that the young people have got
the better of their seniors, and that all the lovely wives *en second noces* have "deceived" their
doddering husbands: but, in spite of the Latin
on the title-page and the rhymes at the end,
the moral lesson inculcated remains a trifle
vague.

4

Congreve to the contrary, this fine gentleman's object is not so much to castigate the
follies of his time with derision, as to perfect
the sort of gallant conversation he forlornly
hoped some day to conduct in real life with
one of his duchesses. Provided his puppets
talk their very best, it does not much matter
how they behave. Unhuman conduct, at all
events, is immaterial in characters created ex-
pressly to voice clever thoughts, since to have
such thoughts is, by ill luck, not generally a
human trait. For nowhere in any drawing-
room was ever spoken anything like Congreve's
dialogue: and his people all live in glass houses
which, very luckily for the tenants, are located

178

in the country that Lamb long ago called the
Utopia of Gallantry. . . The wisest may well
unbend occasionally, to give conscience a half-
holiday, and procure a passport to this delectable land. True, there are, as always in travel,
the custom-house regulations to be observed:
in this realm exist no conscientious scruples, no
probity, no religion, no pompous notions about
altruism, nor any sacred tie of any sort, and
such impedimenta will be confiscated at the
frontier. We are entering a territory wherein
ethics and ideals are equally contraband. For
Congreve's readers make the grand tour of a
new Arcadia, where Strephon wears a peruke,
and Phyllis is arrayed in the latest mode from
the Court of Versailles; and where Priapos, for
all that he remains god of the garden,—about
the formal alley-ways of which flee bevies of
coy nymphs (somewhat encumbered by bro-
caded gowns) pursued by velvet-coated shep-
herds, who carry, in place of vulgar crooks, the
most exquisite of clouded canes,—where the
Lampsacene's statue, I repeat, has been ameliorated into the likeness of a tailor's dummy. It
is a care-free land, where life, untrammeled
by the restrictions of moral codes, untoward
weather, limited incomes or apprehension of

the police, has no legitimate object save the pursuit of amorous pleasures. Allowing for a century of progress and refinement, it is very much the country in which dwelt Marlowe's Hero and Leander.

And probably this atmosphere of holiday detachment from the ordinary duties and obligations of existence is the *milieu* best adapted, after all, to exhilarating comedy. To picture people solely in a temporary and irresponsible withdrawal from the everyday business of life is a serviceable device toward lightheartedness: and you will find that in more recent times a delightful use of it was made by that generally unappreciated artist, Henry Harland. Here is a man whom I have sometimes suspected of a deliberate attempt to reproduce something of this Congrevean atmosphere, as well as almost all the other deliciously improbable conventions of the comedy of Gallantry, in a tale of more modern conditions. Even so, I am free to confess that I once thought Harland's books of more importance than I would care to assert them to-day. For of course it is no longer permissible to believe that, provided the puppets talk their very best, it does not much matter how they behave: and my juniors cow

180

me with their all-devastating "earnestness."

But to revert to Congreve's older chronicles of house-parties and week-ends is to encounter some of the most entertaining company in literature. Thereamong are the fine gentlemen, Careless, and Scandal, and Valentine, and Bellmour, and Mirabell, and the even finer fops, Brisk and Tattle,—magnanimous "Turk Tattle," who, being accidentally married, is honestly grieved, on his wife's account. "The devil take me if I was ever so much concerned at anything in my life. Poor woman! Gad, but I'm sorry for her, too, for I believe I shall lead her a damned sort of life." . . And Lady Froth, and Lady Plyant, and Belinda, and Cynthia, and Angelica, and the well-matched sisters Frail and Foresight, who between them lost and found a bodkin. And the two Witwouds, and Ben Legend, and Lady Wishfort, and Prue, and Sir Sampson, are other names in the list one could go on enumerating, for delight in the pleasant memories evoked. Even for Mrs. Mincing and her unsuccessful endeavors to pin up hair with love-letters in prose, one has a tenderness, and hears with regret how "poor Mincing tift and tift all the morning" . . .

Besides, with Mrs. Mincing, according to the
Stage Directions, enters Mrs. Millamant. . .
It is not easy to say too much in praise of Millamant: for there is nothing in polite comedy that
can pretend to rival her save Célimène, and the
little French widow is not one-tenth so likable,
since the English minx inveigles you into a sort
of fond and half-vexed adoration, from the
moment she appears "in full sail, with her fan
spread and her streamers out, and a shoal of
fools for tenders," till the final settlement of
her heart-affairs, when she has promised to
have Mirabell, on the condition (among so
many others which read more curiously, and
are sufficiently up-to-date to include eugenic
provisos) that "we never visit together, nor
go to the play together, nor call names like love
and sweetheart and the rest of the nauseous
cant, but be as well-bred as if we were not married at all." . . So she vanishes, through a
pleasantly shaded avenue in the St. James's
Park of Utopia: and one envies the lucky fellow as she passes, with mincing steps, painted
and frail under her nodding bows,— "*fardée
et peinte et frèle parmi les nœuds énormes de*

rubans,"—and to the very tips of those slender fingers, which are half-hidden by a gleam of jewels, in everything one sees of her fantastic and adorable. It stays no wonder that Mirabell was confessedly as indulgent to her faults as to his own. For Millamant is not to be remembered as so many paragraphs of printed dialogue: you recollect her as an elfin woman actually seen, heard and capitulated to, because there was no resisting the cool splendor of her eyes (enhanced by a small black star of courtplaster), and the spell of her tinted lips, her sweet and insolent laughter, and, underlying all, her genuine tenderness. . . "None but herself can be her parallel," as Theobald unhappily expressed it, in referring to quite another person: and English comedy has produced nothing else that rivals this brilliant figure.

6

Of course she was the cause that Congreve never married. Having once been intimate with Mrs. Millamant, it was inevitable he should find flesh-and-blood coquettes a little tedious. Indeed, when you deliberate his Utopian seraglio, you cannot but wonder how he managed after his desertion thereof, to put up with thirty years of mere duchesses. . . . The considerate reader will always be in love with Congreve's women; with those lost ladies of a yester-year which was never almanacked; and with the perennial charm of these delectable girls, that never wore rose-tinted flesh. For they are in every thing pre-eminently adorable, these mendacious, subtle, pleasure-loving, babbling, generous, volatile, brave, witty, and sumptuous young jill-flirts who rule in the Utopia of Gallantry. So all true cognoscenti must stay forever enamored of them; of their alert eyes, their little satin-slippered feet, their saucy tip-tilted little noses, their scornful little carmine mouths, and their glittering restless little hands,—for they are all *mignonnes*. Nay, the more discerning will even value them the more for their bright raiment and uncountable fallals,—their stomachers and tight sleeves, their lappets and ribbons, their top-knots and pinners, their lace streamers, and fans, and diamonds, and comfit-boxes; and, above all, that fantastic edifice of hair which rises in tiers and billows and turrets, above their mischievous small faces: whereas Herod of Jewry could not but find something heart-moving in their infinite youth. It is, upon the

184

whole, consoling to reflect that no girls like these were ever confined in impermanent flesh: for then, after setting at most a trio of decades by the ears, they would have grown old, and that tragedy would have been quite unbearable. But since these gallant minxes existed only in romance, their youth remains immortal, and has made glad some seven generations of adorers.

And so, the gravest charge which equity can lay against them is that they spoiled Congreve's interest in all other women. . . . But it will not do too closely to consider what unfilial havoc must have been wrought, off and on, by book-women, in the heart-life of their begetters. Every romantic artist is a Goriot and wastes existence in adoration of his dream daughters as they move in loftier spheres. . . . Meanwhile one may well pity this fond lover's wife. For what chance had poor Ann Shakespeare against Beatrice and Cleopatra and Rosalind? Nor will the judicious deny that Isabella Thackeray lost her mind with considerable provocation when her husband was perpetually closeted now with that red-stockinged jade from Castlewood, and now with the notorious Mrs. Rawdon Crawley. Even Scott's marriage, they say, was not eminently successful: and you may depend upon it that at the bottom of the trouble was one Mistress Diana Vernon of Osbaldistone Hall, in the Cheviots. Indeed, the more perspicacious will have no manner of doubt that Catherine Dickens was driven into a separation through Charles's impending affair with that Wilfer girl, coming as it did upon the heels of his undisguised relations with the first Mrs. Copperfield. . . But all that, too, is a part of the human sacrifice through which Art is yet honored by her zealous servitors. For to be quite contentedly married may be taken as proof positive that a writer has no very striking literary genius, and being unable to outdo nature in creating women, is satisfied to put up with her makeshifts.

7

To Art, then, this William Congreve gave whole-hearted allegiance until he was (like Marlowe) a young fellow of twenty-nine. At that age Congreve also died, as an artist. Physically—and it is toward this fact my pre-amble has from the first been making headway,—physically Congreve survived for some thirty years; and during this period wrote not another line. You will search in vain to find another case

186

which really resembles this. At twenty-nine Congreve was the most famous and most widely admired writer of an age distinguished in letters: and at twenty-nine he put aside literature forever, like a coat of last year's cut. . . .

One perceives that this spruce gambler for immortality found the game not worth the candle. . . . Of the real economy which is practised by the creative writer I have just spoken: yet this unhumanly rational course of life is adopted but as a shield against entire extinction, and proverbially every shield has two sides. I find it on record that the obverse—the not so rational, and therefore more human side—of this buckler against oblivion was fairly presented by another fine literary artist, whose warped soul inhabited the crooked body of Alexander Pope. "Men will remember me. Truly a mighty foundation for pride! when the utmost I can hope for is but to be read in one island, and to be thrown aside at the end of one age. Indeed, I am not even sure of that much. I print, and print, and print. And when I collect my verses into books, I am altogether uncertain whether to look upon myself as a man building a monument or burying the dead. It sometimes seems to me that each publication is but a solemn funeral of many wasted years. For I have given all to the verse-making. Granted that the sacrifice avails to rescue my name from oblivion, what will it profit me when I am dead and care no more for men's opinions?" . . . And Wycherley is asserted to have agreed with the indomitable little hornet of Twickenham. "There was a time," says Wycherley, "when I too was foolishly intent to divert the leisure hours of posterity. But reflection assured me that posterity had, thus far, done very little to place me under that or any other obligation. Ah, no! Youth, health and a modicum of intelligence are loaned to most of us for a while, and for a terribly brief while. They are but loans, and Time is waiting greedily to snatch them from us. For the perturbed usurer knows that he is lending us, perforce, three priceless possessions, and that till our lease runs out we are free to dispose of them as we elect. Now, had I more jealously devoted my allotment of these treasures toward securing for my impressions of the universe a place in yet unprinted libraries, I would have made an investment from which I could not possibly have derived any pleasure, and which would have been to other people of rather dubious benefit."

188

In very much this fashion it would seem that
Congreve reasoned. Like Wycherley, Congreve in his first youth wrote in a manner that
will always delight the elect, because the desire
to write perfectly of beautiful happenings was,
with him also, innate: and throughout all this
thrice-polished writing he presented so irresistibly a plea for what I have called the Gallant
attitude toward life, that in the end he converted himself. One must make the best of this
world as a residence; keep it as far as possible
a cheery and comfortable place; practise urbanity toward the other transient occupants;
and not think too despondently nor too often of
the grim Sheriff, who arrives anon to dispos-
sess you, no less than all the others, nor of any
subsequent and unpredictable legal adjust-
ments:—that is what the creed of Gallantry
came to (long before Congreve played with verbal jewelry under the later Stuarts) when Horace first exhorted well-bred persons to accept
life's inconveniences with a shrug,—*amara lento
temperet risu,*—and to make the most of their
little hour of youth and sunlight in Augustan
Rome; and the Tent-maker sang to very much
that rueful cadence in the Naishápur of Malik
Shah, when the Plantagenets were not yet come

into England. . . . But Congreve was more humanly logical than these elder sceptics, who kept on laboriously refining phrases about the vanity, among so many other vanities, of writing at all. For he devoted thirty very pleasant years to gourmandizing and good wine, and to innumerable lovely women,—who, though not Millamants to be sure, were chosen solely on account of obvious merits, from the green-room and the peerage impartially,—and to reading new books, and to making much brilliant and quite profitless talk with other equally amiable and well-to-do and indolent fine gentlemen. His apostasy to romance, in short, was even more thorough-going than that ecclesiastical abandonment of romance which I just now lamented. And he undertook for the remainder of his life no heavier responsibility than to sign on every quarter-day a receipt for his salary as Secretary of Jamaica, and perhaps every once in a while to wonder where Jamaica might be. . . .

8

Indeed, to all of us who have essayed the word-game, at which one plays for a dole of remembrance in our former lodgings after the Sheriff has haled us hence, there comes at times

190

a dispiriting doubt as to whether the game is worth the candle. Potent and honey-sweet, very certainly, is the allure of this desire to write perfectly of beautiful happenings: for all that, it may well be the contrivance of some particularly sardonic-minded devil: and beyond doubt, if follow the desire you must, you will be the wiser for scrutinizing its logic none too closely. You had best yield blindly to the inborn instinct, and write as well as you possibly can, much as the coral zoophyte builds his atoll, without any theorizing. Assuredly you have not time to count how many candles are being squandered, or what precisely is their value. . . . For here too we cross the trail of another dynamic illusion.

9

Of the *Dive Bouteille* I have spoken at sufficient length. Apart from this sort of sacrifice, however, the literary artist who is really in earnest must be content to do without any number of desirable human traits which he cannot afford. . . . Thus, although modesty may seem to him a most engaging virtue, his mainstay in life must always be an exaggerated and thrice exaggerated opinion of his own value. Should he once admit that what he sets about is by any possibility not the most important thing in the universe, and quite incommensurate by every-day criterions, then his æsthetic grave is already mounded: for the sole alternative is that he writes reading-matter, which is as much as codfish or clocks or honorary college degrees a recognized staple commodity. He has thus his choice between the inconveniencies of appearing to responsible people what is popularly termed a gloomy ass, or of figuring even in his own mind as a verbal huckster. Since write he must, he is restricted either laboriously to pleasure his ideals or his paymasters, and can but pick between being a paranoiac or a prostitute.

Then, too, he must avoid all persons whose tastes are similar to his, and so is condemned to continuous loneliness. Were there nothing else, the romantic artist is a parasite on human life, in the manner of a mistletoe seed, which roots in the oak, draws nutriment therefrom, and so evolves a more delicate type of life, that does but very slightly resemble an oak-tree. And parasites cannot thus nourish one another, nor can the artist come by serviceable notions of ordinary life in the society of his abnormal peers. I grant you that distinguished men of letters have often formed coteries, but it was after their best work was done: and I take it that each fact in part explains the other. Besides, the literary artist who aims to be even more than a valued contributor to magazines, and hopes through ensuing ages to rank above kings, cannot but despise the fellow typist who thinks only of royalties: whereas he is inclined to view his rivals in æsthetic endeavor with very much the complacency of a teased cobra. . . . Thus doomed to live with wholesome folk, the artist cannot afford to make a sane and candid estimate of his work's importance. The tide of circumstance sets so strong against belief in his laborious revisions amounting to anything whatever, that he can but despairingly essay to counterbalance affairs by virtue of a megalomaniac's confidence alike in the worth of what he is resolved to do and in his fitness to perform it immeasurably better than any one else. His daily associates, for whose intelligence (and there is the rub) he cannot but entertain considerable respect, may see clearly enough that art affords in the last outcome a diversion for vacant evenings, or furnishes a museum to which sane people resort only when they accompany their visitors from out-of-town: but of this verdict the artist must not dare to grant the weighty if not absolute justice. In fine, he must be reconciled to having most people think him a fool, and to suspecting that they are not entirely mistaken. . . .

Moreover, the literary artist is condemned to strengthen this belief by means of that very drudgery wherewith he hopes to disprove it. For where other persons decently attempt to conceal their foibles and mistakes and vices, this maniac, stung by the gadfly of self-expression, will catalogue all his and print them in a book. Since write he must, interminably he writes about himself because (in this respect at least resembling the other members of his race) he has no certain knowledge as to anyone else. And the part he has played in other person's lives he will likewise expose in a manner that is not always chivalrous. Indeed, he will undertake much unethical research with the assistance of women who do not entirely comprehend they are participating in a philosophical experiment. And all this, too, he will print in his damned book, for from a social standpoint the creative literary artist is always a traitor, and not infrequently a scoundrel. Meanwhile he becomes callous, by virtue of never yielding so

194

entirely to any emotion as to lose sight of its
being an interesting topic to write about. All
that which is naturally fine in him, in fact, he
will so study, and regard from every aspect,
that from much handling it grows dingy. And
very clearly does the luckless knave perceive
this fact, for all the while, amid these constant
impairments, his vision grows more quick and
keen, and mercilessly shows him the twisted and
scathed thing he is.

10

Nor is this the final jibe. However pleasant it
be to dream of survival in the speech and actions and libraries of posterity, reflection suggests that this "immortality" is deplorably pa-
rochial. For we and our contemporaneous
wasters of shoe-leather and printer's ink, it
may be recalled, are that "posterity" to which
Shakespeare and Milton so confidently addressed themselves: and it were folly to pretend
that to us, as a generation, either of these poets
is to-day, not merely as generally known and
read, but as generally an intellectual influence,
as Mr. Harold Bell Wright or Mrs. Gene Strat-

ton Porter* Of course, a century hence, there will still be a few readers for *Hamlet,* whereas *Freckles*—which is regarded, I believe, as Mrs. Porter's masterpiece—will conceivably be out of print. Yet is it grimly dubious if, in the ultimate outcome of time, the great creative artist exercises more influence, all in all, or is more widely a public benefactor, than is the perpetrator of a really popular novel. . . . I have spoken of the literary artist's patient immolation, which he himself contrives in order that his dream, once snared with comely and fit words, may be perpetuated, and that so the artist may usurp the brain-cells and prompt the flesh of unborn generations. And I have spoken, too, of the *Faustus,* at some length, as the indisputable masterpiece that it is: but suppose you compare its actual aggregate influence upon humanity with the influence, say, of the novel called *Queed* which a few years ago was so extensively purchased. Not even the publishers

*Charteris here refers to two very popular novelists of his day. "It is his almost clairvoyant power of reading the human soul that has made Mr. Wright's books among the most remarkable works of the present age."—*Oregon Journal, Portland.* "It is difficult to speak of the work of Gene Stratton Porter and not to call upon all the superlatives of praise in the language." —*San Francisco Call.*

196

need pretend nowadays that *Queed* was an important contribution to literature: but this book was read by millions, and by many of its readers was naïvely enjoyed and admired and more or less remembered. *Queed* did thus somewhat influence all these honest folk, and tinge their minds, such as they were. Now the *Faustus,* during three centuries of polite speeches about it, has not with any such directness tinged the minds of millions, nor has it been read even by thousands of their own volition. Nor has the *Faustus* ever given that general pleasure which was provoked by *Queed.* And moreover, the "uplifting" optimism of *Queed,* it must be remembered, really brought out that which was best in the readers who took the book seriously. You cannot, of course, evoke from any source more than is already there, and to every end the means must be commensurate: so that, while to bring out the best there is in a wrecked vessel or a gold-mine or a person of some culture requires a deal of elaborated apparatus, a nut-pick will do as much for a walnut, and a popular novel for the average mind. And the point is, that this average mind, which from *Queed* derived enjoyment and some benefit, has (after a brief toleration of the *Faustus* on account of its dreadful "comic" scenes) for some three centuries perceived in Marlowe's masterpiece "just another one of those old classics," and will so view it always. . . . We thus reach by plain arithmetic the proof that as a writer Mr. Sydnor Harrison (who wrote *Queed**) has exercised a greater influence, and has really amounted to more, than Christopher Marlowe: and continuing to be quite honest in our mathematics, we find that as touches influence, neither craftsman can pretend to rival the sympathetic scribe whose daily column of advice to the lovelorn is printed simultaneously by hundreds of our leading public journals, and daily advises millions as to the most delicate and important relations of their existence.

And should you raise the objection that, none the less, the *Faustus* is fine literature, whereas *Queed* is fairly answerable to some other description,—that the drama is profuse in verbal magic, and the novel, to put the matter as civilly as possible, is not remarkable for literary art,—I can but remind you that, after all, your

*"Of all American authors who have made their début in the twentieth century, I regard Mr. Henry Sydnor Harrison as the most promising. . . . Of all our younger writers he seems to have the largest natural endowment."—William Lyon Phelps, in *The Advance of the English Novel* (published 1916).

protest amounts to astonishingly little. All you assert is true enough, but to what, in the high and potent name of St. Stultitia (who presides over the popularity of our reading-matter) does your objection amount? Even to the very, very few who can distinguish between competent work and botchery, the "style" of an adroit writer is apt to become an increasing annoyance, as he proceeds with such miraculous and conscious nicety: until at last you are fretted into active irritation that the fellow does not ever stumble and flounder into some more humanly inadequate way of expressing himself. And for the rest, how many persons really care, or even notice, whether a book be conscientiously written? It is merely "something to read": and they, good souls, have been reduced to looking it over, not quite by any reverential quest of "art," but by a lack of anything else to do.

For literature is a starveling cult kept alive by the "literary." Such literature has been, and will continue to be, always. I grant you that it will continue always. But always, too, its masterworks will affect directly no one save the "literary": and to perceive this is the serious artist's crowning discouragement. For he has every reason to know what "literary" persons are, if but by means of discomfortable introspection, and all and sundry of them he despises. At an Authors' League Dinner, or any similar assemblage of people who "write," you may always detect the participants uneasily peeping toward mirrors, to see if they really do look like the others. . . . And it is only persons such as these, the artist sometimes comprehends forlornly, who will be making any to-do over him a thousand years from to-day! At such depressing moments of prevision, he recognizes that this desire to write perfectly, and thus to win to "literary" immortality, is but another dynamic illusion: and he concedes, precisely as Congreve long ago detected, that, viewed from any personal standpoint, the game is very far from being worth the candle.

VII

THE MOUNTEBANK

—Vastly well, sir! vastly well! a most interesting gravity! . . .

—He is very perfect indeed! Now, pray what did he mean by that?

—Why, by that shake of the head, he gave you to understand that even though they had more justice in their cause, and wisdom in their measures—yet, if there was not a greater spirit shown on the part of the people, the country would at last fall a sacrifice to the hostile ambition of the Spanish monarchy.

—The devil! did he mean all that by shaking his head?

—Every word of it—if he shook his head as I taught him.

—*The Critic*

VII
Which Indicates the Mountebank

B
UT it occurs to me that I have thus far
spoken of Gallantry as a force in literature. That is, past doubt, its most important aspect, since literature is compounded of so
much finer material than life, and is builded so
much more durably, that it affords the worthier
field of exercise for any and all ideas. But of
course when the spirit of Gallantry was expressed in books, man continued as always to
play the ape to his dreams, and clumsily began
to reproduce the fantasies of Wycherley and
Congreve in everyday conduct. Thus it was in
the eighteenth century that Gallantry found its
most adequate exposition in actual life, which
is customarily at least a generation behind its
current reading-matter. And concerning a peculiarly striking instance of this vital imitative-
ness I must for a moment digress, before explaining its very poignant relevancy to what I
have in mind as to another dynamic illusion.

Indeed, in the eighteenth century men were reading much of that depressing literature for which the unborn Victorians were to furnish illustrations. In letters the exit of Mrs. Millamant seemed to have marked both the apex and the final curtain of the comedy of Gallantry. After Congreve, and his colleagues Vanbrugh and Farquahar, as no doubt you remember, follows that dreary interval wherein dramatic art floundered and splashed, and eventually drowned, in a stagnant pond of morality. This was the heyday of "do-me-good, lackadaisical, whining, make-believe comedies." For now it was to the responsibilities of actual life that comedy of Sentiment attempted to resign the spirit, and the comedy of Gallantry seemed in a fair way to give up the ghost. Then life made a fine plagiarism, and enriched zoology by reproducing in flesh and blood the manifestly impossible *jeune premier* of the comedy of Gallantry. . . .

2

In consequence, some three-quarters of a century after Mrs. Millamant "dwindled into a wife," a youth of twenty made his appearance at Bath, possessed of no resources save good looks, a tolerable supply of impudence, and—life being resolved to do the thing thoroughly,—a translation of Aristænetus. By virtue of these assets Dick Sheridan forthwith becomes the ruler of that mixed company of valetudinarians and dowagers, of second-rate bucks and fortune-hunters, retired army-officers, and ladies of rank "chiefly remarkable for the delicacy of their reputations." Brilliant, young and victorious, he has only to appear in order to be admired. In the Pump-room there is no dandy who attracts more attention than "handsome Dick": and it is in accordance with his election that the trousered portion of Bath society models its cravats. . . .

Nor was he less popular among women. His manner toward them, it is recorded, had just the proper blending of respect and audacity. No one could say more impudent things with a greater air of humility. Here was a macaroni who made love-verses and love with equal grace, however rarely these perilous accomplishments are united in one artist. . . . Then, too, to a woman the poet who appeals to her vanity is one thing, and the lover who touches her heart quite another: for the rhymester, while pleasing and appropriate for rare occasions, is a trifle outlandish for everyday wear. Besides, the average woman is bored by poetry, if only because girl-children proverbially inherit the tastes of their fathers. So Daphne, wise in her generation, fled the embraces of Apollo, and her sisters have followed the example, to the enrichment of the world's literature by an infinity of wailing sonnets. . . . But Sheridan's love-verses are really exquisite trifles, without the least taint of sincerity; and so, it may be that they did not greatly hinder him in winning the heart of Maria Linley, the reigning belle of Bath, "upon whom Nature seemed to have lavished her richest treasures, and by the example of her generosity to have roused Art to noble emulation." Certain it is, by whatever means he attained Miss Linley's favor, that Sheridan succeeded in making fools of some ten or twelve other suitors, and in eloping with the young lady to Paris, in the true style of Gallant comedy. There they were married: and on their return to England Sheridan, still in the rôle of *jeune premier,* fought two duels with one of his outwitted rivals. . . . Throughout, as you will remember, he treated the entire affair as being a frolic; and—with just the appropriate dramatic touch,—invited his antagonist to sup with him and the seconds the night before they met in battle. The invitation was declined, which seems almost a pity: and the encounter, of course, was not lethal, since life was plagiarising from the comic stage. . . .

So began the series of improbable scenes in which Sheridan was to figure as the hero. Being, as he entirely comprehended, cast for the part, he enacted it with sufficient sentiment to render him attractive to the audience, and with enough variety to prevent the attitudinizing growing tiresome to him: and it is as a piece of histrionic art that we ought to judge the life of Sheridan. . . . Thus at first he is the *jeune premier* of the comedy; a handsome mountebank, no better than he should be perhaps, but making, in his embroidered coat and red-heeled shoes, a prodigiously pleasing figure. So the young rogue struts in the sunlight,—profoundly conscious that the men all run after him, and none of the women can resist him. Misbehaving himself he is, of course, and having a delightful time of it, too. And he is perfectly content, as yet, to let more prudent people say

whatever they will, and croak any number of
warnings as to the follies of this world provid-
ing fuel for the next, because after all he is not
committing any enormities. He is the *jeune
premier* of the comedy: and at the bottom of
our hearts the majority of us can find a sneak-
ing fondness, and a fund of sympathy, for this
graceless youth, who has thus far manifested no
nobler desire than that of outshining his fellow
dandies, and no more elevated notion of happiness than a "wet" night at the tavern. . . . It
is the attitude which romance has taught us to
adopt toward the sowers of wild oats, and reason has nothing to do with it.

3

With marriage, the mountebank entered the
larger world of London, and turned playwright,
as a temporary makeshift to help meet the expenses of that fine establishment in Portman
Square he had just set up on credit. Within
five years he thus completed and produced six
potboilers: and three of these were masterworks. . . . Sheridan was the very last ad-
herent of "that laughing painted French bag-
gage, the Comic Muse who came over from the
Continent with Charles, after the Restoration,"

—a not-immaculate nymph, who, as we have
seen had been blithe and rather shameless in her
traffic with Wycherley and Congreve: but her
merriment is less free now that she inspires
The Rivals and *The School for Scandal.* De-
cidedly, one reflects, her stay in England has improved the minx: there is a kindlier sound to
her voice, and her laughter echoes with a heart-
ier ring. She remains audacious, and retains
her rouge and gauds: but under all the tinsel
and frippery beats a generous wild loving human heart. . . . So you reflect, in spite of
yourself: for this mountebank-artist, Sheridan,
knows perfectly well the value of what publishers describe without compunction in private
converse, and glowingly commend in type as
"wholesome sentiment."

It was a clever schoolboy who defined a pla-
giarist as "a writer of plays." Sheridan has
taken an idea from George Villiers, a character
from Fielding, a situation from Molière, and so
on, with the light fingers of an inveterate bor-
rower: he has mingled all, and has flavored the
mixture with jests of his own compounding and
of his neighbor's: the materials are mostly stolen, yet the ragout is unmistakably Sheridan's.
And though he confessedly write potboilers, he

is no hasty composer nor careless workman:
for in this man too was inborn that irrational
desire to write perfectly: and these speeches
which come off so airily, and these scenes that
seem written at whiteheat, were laboriously constructed, and revised, and polished and re-pol-
ished to the very last degree of refinement, before the author exposed them to the glare of
footlights. For it is still possible to consult
Sheridan's rough drafts of all this sprightly
elegance, and they read queerly enough. . . .
Here is one Solomon Teazle, a widower who
has lost five children, and talks over his wife's
extravagance with the butler: before Sheridan
has done with him this Teazle will have entered
knighthood, as Sir Peter, and immortality will
bestow the accolade. Here is Solomon's ill-
bred, stupid and impertinent wife,—who when
she steps upon the stage will be that Lady Teazle who so gracefully poignarded reputations,
and led the van of a regiment of misunderstood
heroines toward discovery in an unmarried
man's apartments by their husbands. . . . And
so the tale goes. Over and over again Sheridan
wrote and re-wrote his potboilers until they
were masterpieces. The point is that to the considerate person it is well-nigh pathetic to de-

tect this splendid mountebank taking so much pains over anything. . . . And then, like Congreve, he recognized that the word-game is not worth the candle. "Deuce take posterity!" he is reported to have summed it up. "A sensible man will bear in mind that all this world's delicacies are to be won, if ever, from one's contemporaries. And people are generous toward social rather than literary talents, for the sensible reason that they derive more pleasure from an agreeable companion at dinner than from having a rainy afternoon rendered endurable by some book or another."

So the mountebank very sensibly turned man of affairs,—just as in comedy the scapegrace son is prone to astound everybody and outwit his delighted father by disclosing unsuspected business ability,—and, with borrowed money, purchased his own theatre. A trifle later (and again with borrowed money) he bought a seat in Parliament, and set up as a statesman. And that was the end of his career in letters, for as an artist Sheridan also, by a quaint coincidence, perished at twenty-nine. . . .

Meanwhile it is a brilliant literary feast which the youth of this mountebank purveyed. The lights are all rose-color, the wine is good (though borrowed and unpaid for), the women are beautiful, and all the men have wit. You cannot but delight in this assemblage of light-hearted persons, and in the prevailing glitter, which is gem-like, beyond doubt, and yet is unaccountably suggestive of rhinestones. . . .

There is no denying that the funeral pyre of the comedy of Gallantry blazed very notably in the wit of Sheridan. Yet *The Rivals* and *The School for Scandal*, brilliant as they are, can hardly be ranked with Congreve's verbal pyrotechnics in *The Way of the World* and *The Double-Dealer*. Nor is the comparison quite fair, since Sheridan's plays are, from æsthetic standpoints, too disastrously handicapped by the strivings of their author, as though this were a necessary part of his emulation of the highest social circles, to wed the incompatible. This splendid mountebank has made deliberate attempt to blend the old school with the new, and to infuse into the comedy of Gallantry "a wholesome sentiment." It is unnecessary to point out that the demand for such literary treacle has always been unfailing, and that auctorial mountebanks have always done therein a thriving trade: Euripides dispensed such sweetmeats in Athens very anciently, and in

212

American publishers' lists the Cinderella legend masquerades perennially as a new novel.
. . . Here the results are those dialogues between Julia and Faulkland,—the love-scenes which made *The Rivals* a popular success, and which nowadays we condone because they are omitted in representation, and there is no statute compelling anyone to read them. For here the rhinestone glitter is at its cheapest. "When hearts deserving happiness would unite their fortunes, Virtue would crown them with the unfading garland of modest hurtless flowers; but ill-judging Passion will force the gaudier rose into the wreath, whose thorn offends them when its leaves are dropped." Really, for anyone who concludes a masterpiece of comedy in just that fashion there would seem to be no punishment quite severe enough: and yet the dictates of "wholesome sentiment" have elsewhere brought about conclusions even more flagrant, and continue to breed remunerative inanities.
. . . . Many of us are not a little grateful for the fact that in writing *The School for Scandal* Sheridan steered an ingenious middle-course, and caused Charles Surface and Maria to do all their love-making before the play began. Their brief encounter at the end is inoffensive: and

the judicious will pass very lightly over the sop thrown to sentiment in the reforming wastrel's pentametric outburst.

4

So the mountebank gave up literature, and became a man of affairs. . . . And with him went a continual glitter, as of rhinestones. Than Mr. Sheridan, the owner of Drury Lane Theatre, there was for thirty years no Mæcenas more courted and conspicuous. True, he was overwhelmed with lawsuits, he made it a business-rule never to open a business-letter, and the salaries of his actors and carpenters and multitudinous employees were always long overdue. But he catered unerringly to the popular taste, and when there was any pressing need he could always talk his bankers into another loan. At Brooke's and Almack's there was no gamester more determined, nor anyone more ready to wager any sum on any hazard. Thus he wins and loses fortunes overnight, and often has not a shilling in his pocket. Meanwhile, he lives in splendor, "as a statesman and a man of fashion who 'set the pace' in all pastimes of the opulent and idle": and the Prince-Regent is proud to be seen with Mr. Sheridan, for this mountebank retained men's admiration as a vested right. . . . No one resists him, and nothing daunts the fellow, not even when fire destroys the theatre in which was invested every penny of all the money he had borrowed. To any other man the loss would mean double ruin: but Mr. Sheridan loiters in the Bedford Coffee-House over the way, point-de-vice in every solitaire and lace ruffle, smiling a little, and chatting with the assembled pleasure-seekers there, as he watches the flames; and he calls for liquid refreshments, upon the plea, no longer considered valid, that a man may reasonably be permitted to take a glass of wine by his own fireside. . . . When misfortunes overwhelm him, as he knows by experience, he somehow floats out of the welter like a cork. This destruction of the theatre thus means very little to him, who has only to borrow a few more thousands of pounds, and re-build. For he is always borrowing, with the air of one performing an act of friendship. The luckless tradesmen, it is related, call to bully him into payment of long-standing debts, and end by inducing him to accept a monetary loan. A glib tongue and imperturbable self-assurance are his equipments in battle with the world: but he makes them serve, and prodigally.

And perhaps these weapons are as much as anybody really needs. . . .

Even with his wife they served prodigally. Maria Sheridan lived under the spell of her husband's bounce and glitter, through twenty-one years of married life, and died adoring him. 'Twas a matter of large comment by the town that Mr. Sheridan's grief was prodigiously edifying: for in this, too, he somewhat outdid nature. . . . He was now a time-battered rake nearing fifty, and bereft of his good looks by dissipation, but still perfect in manner and apparel and assurance. So he re-married, selecting, as a matter of course, the most prepossessing young heiress of the day,—"the irresistible Ogle," as she was toasted,—and winning the Dean of Winchester's daughter amid circumstances which were sufficiently curious. . . .

Meanwhile in Parliament he encounters the first orators of the time, and outtalks them. His arraignment of Warren Hastings, the impeached governor-general of India, is the sensation of the age: at the conclusion of Mr. Sheridan's opening speech the House is adjourned, so that the members can regain control of their overwrought emotions. When he rises to continue, a seat in the visitors' gallery costs fifty

216

guineas, and the gallery is full. Mr. Sheridan spoke for three days, with what was everywhere conceded to be unparalleled brilliancy. When he had done, the lawyer who was there to defend Hastings vehemently protested his client to be a monster of iniquity. I do not expect you to believe this, but it is a matter of record. The great Pitt (who, mark you, very cordially detested Mr. Sheridan) admits that "this speech surpassed all the eloquence of ancient or modern times, and possessed everything that genius or art could furnish to agitate and control the human mind." Burke asserted the oration to be "the most astonishing effort of eloquence, argument and wit united, of which there was any record or tradition." And Fox declared that "all he had ever heard, all he had ever read, when compared with this speech, dwindled into nothing, and vanished like vapor before the sun." In short, there was never such a Parliamentary triumph. . . . And of course these invectives against Hastings (whose main crime lay in being a Tory) were claptrap of quite astounding commonplaceness, as any man can see for himself who cares to endure the tedium of reading these speeches; but they dazzled all England, and served the

mountebank's turn to admiration. He becomes
secretary of foreign affairs, secretary of the
treasury, treasurer of the navy, and so on, holding office after office, and purchasing every advancement with pinchbeck oratory. Before each
speech it was his custom to drink a pint of
brandy ''neat.'' But there was no resisting Mr.
Sheridan, not even when he was sober. . . .
From beginning to end, his career is an extrava-
ganza such as no thoughtful artist would care
to perpetrate: and you cannot but feel that in
producing him life laid too onerous a strain
upon belief.

Thus far the drama has sped so trippingly
that one rather boggles over the last act. . . .
It would appear that life was fumbling at some
lugubrious moral. If not as apologue, how
else are we to interpret this bloated old Silenus,
this derelict who has outlived alike his health,
his income, his friends, his talents, and his reputation? By retaining the Prince-Regent's
friendship he might have lived to the last in
that continuous rhinestone glitter. But Wales
wanted help just then in the matter of securing
his divorce. ''Sir,'' said Mr. Sheridan, ''I never
take part against a woman,''—and with that
flourish went to his ruin gallantly. . . . Yet this

218

sudden eclipse of Sheridan, with its brief **and**
painful sequel, was not æsthetically allowable:
it was bad art: and the comedy straggled out
into an intolerable fiasco when the greatest wit
in Europe, and probably the most polished
mountebank therein, became so broken-spirited
that he wept at a compliment and grew pale at
the sight of a constable. . . . Dukes and mar-
quises bore his coffin to Westminster Abbey,
and they buried him with princely honors: but
he died an imbecile, happily unconscious that
the sheriff's officer was threatening to drag him
off, in the blankets, to the debtors' prison. . . .
Yes, it must be that life was fumbling at a
moral, of just that explicit sort which every
writer worth his salt knows to be unforgivably
artificial. . . .

5

Meanwhile, from a variety of standpoints, it
is salutary to consider Sheridan's career. As
an instance of life's not quite successful plagiarism from literature, it has been discussed
sufficiently. But moreover, I would have you
mark that for the thirty-two years he adorned
Parliament this mountebank was taken quite

seriously, and without any harm coming thereof. He was very often too drunk to walk, but as secretary of foreign affairs he guided a nation acceptably. He was never within sight of paying his debts, or even of guessing what they might amount to, so the Coalition ministry made him secretary of the treasury. And finally, at a period when Britannia, as a circumstance of considerable choric notoriety, ruled the waves, he who was equally ignorant of finance and maritime matters was treasurer of the navy. Sheridan was as profoundly and it would seem as obviously unqualified as dictionaries could well express to fill any of the offices given him: and he discharged their duties perfectly. Had he died at sixty his career would have been the most immoral chapter in recorded history: and it is solely by virtue of his injudiciousness in living three years longer that reputable persons are to-day enabled to face this mountebank's continuous success. . . . His secret merely was to pretend to be what seemed expected. And for divers reasons nobody ever exposed him. . . .

I shall digress into plain egotism. The initial indiscretion of my life made me the youngest of a large family, and, while I have sunk to authorship, my step-brothers and sisters have turned out remarkably well. They are responsible citizens, authorities on business and the stock-market and cognate riddles, eminent in local politics, leaders in education, and one of them is a much admired clergyman whose eloquence soars fearlessly to the loftiest platitudes. Yet as a matter of fact, I know they are still the children with whom I used to play in a brick-paved backyard, about and under a huge cat-alpa tree. . . . Each has come by an official manner, like a grave mask in which to earn bread and butter, and otherwise further the wearer's desires: this laid aside, in family gatherings, you will find that each displays as to any matter outside of his recognized vocation very little interest and no ideas whatever. At most, in regard to the rest of life each of my brothers and sisters cherishes a handful of erro-neous catchwords acquired by tenth-hand hear-say. . . . For mentally they have developed hardly at all: they are those children with whom I used to play, incarcerated in matured bodies, as I perceive to my daily astonishment: and the world at large permits these children to meddle with its important causes and its cash and its spiritual welfare. . . . In fact, they are en-

221

couraged to do so: and like Sheridan, they appear somehow to meet the responsibility in a perfectly adequate fashion. For they pass as models of acumen and reliability: and only by accident do I know that when my serious-minded kindred look most imposing they are meditating trivialities or else not thinking about anything at all. . . . Do I appear to accuse them of stupidity? Well, I confess I have heard my preacher-brother publicly assert that war was the final method of proving, not which side had the stronger army, but that we were right: and my banker-brother once informed me it was a striking proof of God's kindness that He had given all the larger seaports excellent harbors. When voiced by one's own flesh, such imbecilities wake self-distrust. And yet, I cannot but admiringly recognize that my kindred are persons of exceptional success in the practical affairs of life, as these matters are conducted. For my kindred very convincingly pretend to be what seems expected. . . .

6

And to me who wonder at the irrationality of all this, to me also, life has been an interminable effort to pretend to be what seemed expected. I know quite well at bottom that I too have very little changed from what I was in boyhood, when for any say in matters of import I was concededly unfit. But there is no arguing with the looking-glass, and it displays a rather sagacious-seeming person. . . . None the less, the outcome is really too preposterous that I should have acquired a house and a bank-account, a wife and children, and a variety of other valuables that ought to be entrusted only to responsible people. And when I think of the ignorance and incapacity I daily endeavor to conceal, and all the baseless pretensions and unreal interests I affect hourly, it appals me to reflect that very possibly everyone else conducts affairs on a not dissimilar plan. For I have suffered as yet no open detection. The neighbors seem to accept me quite gravely as the head of a family: the chauffeur touches his cap and calls me "sir": publishers bring out my books: and my wife fair-mindedly discusses with me all our differences of opinion, so that we may without any bitterness reach the compromise of doing what she originally suggested. I even serve on juries, and have a say in whether or no a full-grown man shall go to jail. . . .

Some day, I think, this playing at responsibility will be ended. In some unguessable fashion the years will be turned back, and I shall be nineteen or thereabouts concededly, and shall no longer be disguised by scanty hair and wrinkled flesh and this interminable need of pretending to be a noteworthy and grave person. At the bottom of my heart I know that the trappings of a staid citizen have been given me through some mistake,—his house and wife and motors and farm-lands and table-silver, and his graying moustache and rheumatic twinges and impaired digestion, and his mannerisms and little dignities and continual small fussy obligations,—and that the error will have to be set right. These things are alien to me: and instinctively I know that my association with them is temporary. And so it will be managed somehow that these things will pass from me, as a piled cloud-heap passes, and I shall enter again into a certain garden, and find therein a girl whom I and one aging woman alone remember. It is toward that meeting all things move, quite irresistibly, and all life turns as a vast wheel, so very slowly, till time has come full-circle through this stupefying mist of common-sense and even more common prejudice. For life, if life means anything,

224

must aim toward realities: and that girl and boy, and that garden and their doings therein, were more important and more real to me, as I know now, than things have been since then. . . . Nothing, indeed, that happens after nineteen or thereabouts can ever be accepted as quite real, because the person to whom it happens can no longer meet it frankly. There is no thorough contact between the event and his flinching wary senses. For always the need of judicious reservation, the feeling of amenability to what is expected of you, and in fine the obligation of being a mountebank, conspire to prevent entire surrender to reality: and there is a prescribed etiquette, of which some underthought is more or less potent in all we say or do. At times, indeed, this etiquette controls us absolutely, as in matters of personal honor or in love-making, so that we recite set phrases and move as puppets. Thus we worry graveward, with the engagement of but a part of our faculties: and we no longer participate in life with all our being.

7

So it is that the accepted routine of life's conduct tends to make mountebanks of us inevitably: and the laborious years weave small hypocrisies like cobwebs about our every action, and at last about our every thought. The one consoling feature is that we are so incessantly busied at concealment of our personal ignorance and incapacity as to lack time to detect one another. For we are all about that arduous task: at every moment of our lives we who are civilized persons must regard, if we indeed do not submit to be controlled by, that which is expected of us: and we are harassed always by an instant need of mimicking the natural behavior of men as, according to our generally received if erroneous standards, "men ought to be." It all reverts, you observe, to the æsthetic canons of Sophocles. . . . And not the least remarkable part of the astounding business is that this continuous pretending by everybody appears to answer fairly well. It passes the pragmatic test: it works, and upon the whole it works without bringing about intolerable disaster. . . . Yet it is interesting to observe the unaccountability of many of these conformances to what is expected, and to wonder if, as I have suggested, our standards may by any chance be here and there erroneous. I am often surprised by what does seem expected of us, through the

entire irrelevance of the thing indicated to our
formula for expressing it. . . .

For instance, I am expected to amuse myself.
One way of doing this is to preface my pleasure-
seeking by putting on, among other habiliments,
a cuirass of starched linen,—a stubborn and
exacerbating garment, with no conceivable palliation,—and a funereal-hued coat, with elon-
gated tails, of which the only use is to prevent
my sitting down with comfort. Thus calami-
tously equipped, I set forth unabashed by the
gaze of heaven's stars, to an uncarpeted room
where a band is playing, place my right hand
toward the small of a woman's back,—who has
bared her arms and shoulders in preparation
for the ceremony,—hold her left hand in mine,
and in this posture escort her around the room,
not once but time after time. At intervals a
reputable lawyer, under no suspicions as to his
sanity, blows a child's whistle, and the woman
and I, with others, take part in a sort of military drill. After I have repeated this process,
over and over again, with several women, all of
us go into another room and eat a variety of
indigestible things within an allotted time,
somewhat as though we were lunching at one
of those rural railway stations where the pas-

sengers forage for sandwiches and pie and chicken while the train waits restively. We then return to the first apartment, and proceed with the original form of evolutions until several hours of yet another calendar day are disposed of. . . . There is no great harm in all this, and in fact, the physical exercise involved may be mildly beneficial, if not offset by indigestion. The impenetrable mystery remains, though, how the cotillion, or dancing in any form, came to be employed as an arbitrary symbol for amusement. . . . But, indeed, now that we elderly people are no longer encouraged to become mildly intoxicated at all social gatherings, I am afraid the truth is being forced upon us that man, after age has bred discernment, can get but little delight from the company of his fellows when in his sober senses. . . .

Or put it that I am expected to evince my religious faith. I must set about this by putting on my best raiment,—for, again like children, we need must "dress up" for everything we "play at,"—and by going into a building, of which the roof is indecorously adorned with a tall phallic symbol, and by remaining there for an hour and a half. There too we perform a drill, of standing, sitting and kneeling, and we read and sing archaic observations from little books. Sometimes the formulæ we repeat are not unastounding, as when we gravely desiderate the privilege of dipping our feet in the blood of our enemies, or even request that our adversaries be forthwith carried alive into hell. An honest gentleman, whose conduct upon weekdays I cordially revere, emerges from the vestry, in what to the unsophisticated might appear to be a collocation of the fragments of a black bathrobe and of a nightgown; and after forbidding us to worship stone images (which really does seem rather a superfluous exhortation) announces that the Neighborhood League will meet on Monday evening, and devotes some twenty minutes to revising one or another well-meant utterance of Christ into conformity with more modern ideas. Then plates are passed, into which we put envelopes containing money, to pay for the heating, lighting and general upkeep of the building, and the living expenses of the clergyman and the janitor. Now all this is likewise more or less harmless, yet, sanely viewed, it is difficult to connect in any way with religion. . . .

But the tale of our grave-faced antics is interminable. . . . I meet So-and-so, and we inquire simultaneously, "How do you do?" without either of us giving or expecting an answer. We shake hands, for the perhaps inadequate reason that several centuries ago people did this to show that neither of them was carrying a knife. And thereupon we babble of topics concerning which both know the verdict of either to be valueless, such as the lessening supply of good servants and the increasing cost of food, or the probability of rain and what our wives are planning to do. And I find myself advancing opinions I never thought of holding, just to make conversation to which neither of us pays any particular attention. I find myself gravely expounding what I remember paying for shoes, and from what direction storms usually approach our house, and our reasons for spending the summer in one place rather than another, quite as if these were matters about which my hapless listener might conceivably want to know. What curse is come upon me, I marvel inly, that I must discourse such nonsense? and why, in heaven's name, should this man be telling me about his automobile and what he said to the butler? Then, when we say "good-bye," we sedately invoke in that contracted form the guardianship of Omnipotence for each other.

230

. . . The transaction throughout is automatic, for of course we do not actually think of what we are in point of fact saying and doing: and indeed the majority of us appear to get through life quite comfortably without thinking at all. For consider how very generally we believe that we—who have eyes, too,—are a race of "white" persons; and that the promises of the Marriage Ceremony are such as may be made rationally; and that it is a matter of course arrangement to pay taxes for the privilege of retaining what confessedly belongs to you; and that it preserves justice to execute a murderer, on the principle that two homicides constitute a maintenance of what one of them upsets; and that it is humorous to mention certain towns, such as Oshkosh or Kankakee, and is somehow an excellent joke on anyone to have a baby or a mother-in-law: so that, in fine, we are guided in well-nigh every transaction in life by axioms and presumptions which have not even the lean merit of sounding plausible. . . .

8

But it is not merely that our private lives are given over to mental anarchy. . . . We live under a government which purports to be based, actually, on the assumption that one man is as good as another. No human being believes this assumption to be true, of course, nor could any form of polity that took it seriously survive a week: but the imposing statement serves well enough as the ostensible cornerstone of democracy. And we must all regard the laws of this government, since to one or another of these laws must be amenable every action of our lives. Thus you may well spare time to visit a legislative body in session, and to listen to the debates, and to conjecture whether each participant is really an imbecile or for ulterior ends is consciously making a spectacle of himself. However, it may be an excess of modesty which induces the self-evident belief of every public speaker that the persons who have assembled to hear him cannot possibly be intelligent. And if you will attend a State Legislature, in particular, and look about you, and listen for a while, and reflect that those preposterous people are actually making and unmaking laws by which your physical life is ordered, you will get food for wonder and some perturbation. But of course, poor creatures, they too are trying to do what seems expected of them, very much as

Sheridan attacked Warren Hastings: and many of the most applauded public speakers conserve an appreciable degree of intelligence for private life.

When you consider that presidents and chief-justices and archbishops and kings and states-men are human beings like you and me and the state legislators and the laundryman, the thought becomes too horrible for humanity to face. So, here too, romance intervenes promptly, to build up a mythos about each of our promi-nent men,—about his wisdom and subtlety and bravery and eloquence, and including usually his Gargantuan exploits in lechery and drunken-ness,—so as to save us from the driveling terror that would spring from conceding our destinies in any way to depend on other beings quite as mediocre and incompetent as ourselves. . . .

9

Yet perfection graces few human subterfuges. Thus very often does the need arise for romance to preserve us yet further, from discovering that this protective talk of "statesmanship" and "policies" is nonsense clamorously ex-ploded. For sometimes nations come to fisticuffs, just as inconsequently as the plumber and the baker might do, and the neighbors take part, very much as a street-row intensifies, until a considerable section of the world is devastated. Then romance prompts us, in self-protection, to moralize of one or the other side's "aims" and "plottings" and "schemes," and so on, as the provokers of all this ruin, rather than acknowledge the causes to lie disconcertingly deeper, and to be rooted in our general human incompetence, and in our lack of any especial designs whatever. . . . Never at any time is man in direr need of disregarding men as they are, than under the disastrous illumination of war: for then actually to face the truth would forthwith drive anyone of us insane. We are then all shuddering through a disrupted Vanity Fair of mountebanks who have come to open and ignominous failure: and our sole hope of salvation lies in pretending not to notice. For it sometimes happens that among these so cruelly exposed mountebanks are our own chosen overlords, chosen as such, for the most part, on account of their real superiority to the run of men: and when this happens, the more perspicacious among us prefer not to recognize our overlords' incompetence, because we know that these pathetic muddlers and blusterers represent, upon the whole, the best our race is yet able to produce. . . .

So it is rather sad when war breaks out, and honored subterfuges unaccountably collapse. Everyone was letter-perfect in what seemed expected of him under the old order: but when that is upset overnight, and there are no standards to conform to, nobody anywhere has any notion what to do. It breeds a seizure of dumb panic which is unbearable. So—kings and cabinets and generalissimos being at a nonplus, and even presidents (in Mexico and other Southern republics) falling a shade short of omniscience, —the nations flounder, and gabble catchwords, and drift, and strike out blindly, and tergiversate, and jostle one another, and tell frantic falsehoods, and hit back, like fretful children; and finally one by one fling aside the last trammeling vestige of reason and self-control, and go screaming mad (with a decided sense of relief) in order to get rid of the strain. And so spreads steadily the holocaust. . . .

Yes, it is rather sad, because you cannot but suspect that whatever befalls a race of such attested incompetence cannot very greatly matter if the universe be conducted on any serious basis. Yet even in war-time men worry along somehow, desperately endeavoring still to live up to notions derived from romantic fiction, such as is provided by public speakers and newspaper editorials and the censored war-news,—and liberally ascribing "plans" and "policies" to every accident of the carnage, and revising these explanations as often as seems expedient. We play, in fine, that human intelligence somewhere either has the situation in hand or at least foresees a plausible way out of it. We are thus never actually reduced to facing the truth: for however near we may blunder to the verge of such disaster, the demiurge protects us by means of that high anæsthesia which we term "patriotism."

10

Now patriotism is, of course, something more than a parade of prejudice, so flimsy that even at the height of its vogue, in war-time, anyone of us can see the folly, and indeed the wickedness, of such patriotism as is manifested by the other side. For with our own country's entry into war, it is generally conceded that, whether for right or wrong and in default of any coherent explanation by our overlords as to what we are doing in that fighting galley, we can all agree to stand together in defence of our national honor. In large part, this is another case of doing what seems to be expected: and the vast majority of us begin by being patriotically bellicose in speech out of respect to our neighbor's presumed opinion, while he returns the courtesy. So we both come at last unfeignedly to believe what we are saying, just as men always find conviction in repetition: and a benevolent wave of irrationality sweeps over towns and cross-roads, with the most staid of us upon its crest excitedly throwing tea into Boston Harbor, or burning effigies of Lincoln and Davis (severally, as taste directs), or trampling upon Spanish flags, and organizing parades and passing resolutions, and even attempting to memorize our national air. . . . Doubtless, all this is grotesque, upon the surface, and is of no especial use in settling the war: but it prevents us from thinking too constantly of the fact that we are sending our boys to death. . . . The demiurge, in fine, to soothe bewilderment and panic administers patriotism as an anæsthetic. And as has been pointed out, elsewhere, we find that ardent patriotism can even be made to serve as an exhilarating substitute for lukewarm religion whenever the two happen to be irreconcilable. . . . Each war, in short, with its attendant outlets for new energies, arouses a fine if not quite explicable general sense of doing something of real importance, in all save the emotionally abstemious, to whom any war must perforce appear in its inception a gloomy error, and in its manifestations a nuisance.

And probably these thin-blooded people are wrong. Æsthetically, at any rate, there is a deal to be said in favor of patriotism, and of this quaint-seeming faith in the especial merits of one's own country and in all the curious customs of one's country, however inexplicable, even though this faith occasionally convert Earth into a revolving shambles. For patriotism is, of course, not merely an anæsthetic: to the contrary, it is, like all the other magnanimous factors in human life, a dynamic product of the demiurge. Thus patriotism (as Paul Vanderhoffen has put it) can ascend to lofty heights without depending upon logic to give it a leg up. To prefer your country's welfare to your own is rational enough, since it is but to assume that the whole is greater than the part: but when we proceed to prefer our country's welfare to that of any and all other countries in the world,—as we unanimously do, with the glowing approval of conscience,—we must progress by high-mindedly reversing the original assumption. So that patriotism is undefiled by any smirch of "realism" or of that which is merely "logical,"—and must always be kept thus in order to stay vigorous, since patriotism is a product, and one of the most generally commended products, of the demiurge.

And I, for one, find nothing unreasonable in the irrationality of patriotism. . . . The other animals munch grass and paw at unconsidered dirt, where man not all unconsciously gets nourishment from his mother's bosom. For we know ourselves to be born of that coign of Earth we cherish with no inexplicable affection. Not only in spirit does our habitat conform us, since the land we love, that soil whereon our cattle graze, goes steadily to the making of plants, and thence becomes incarnate in our bodies: until we ourselves seem but a many agglutinate and animated particles of that land we love, with such partiality as we may not rouse toward those cool abstractions, equity and logic, but reserve for our corporal kin. Thus patriots may rationally justify the direst transports of their ac-

239

tions, if not the wisdom of their public utterances. For in battling for the honor of one's birthplace each hand is lifted in defence, not merely of opinions, but of the very field in which it once was dust: and he that is slain does but repay through burial a loan from his mother. So it is with actual and very profound reason that we are not reasonable about the display of our patriotism: for no man, of whatever nationality, is called on to be reasonable where his mother's welfare appears concerned or, to however small degree, her honor seems impugned. In such a quandary he strikes. The merits of his cause he will defer for later consideration. And meanwhile wisdom and philosophy may speak with the tongue of angels, and be hanged to them: for the noble madness of patriotism pleads at quite another tribunal, and addresses the human heart, whereover neither ear nor brain has jurisdiction. Our mother seems to be molested; and we strike to requite all those who trouble her, no matter what be their excuse. That only is the immediate essential: long afterward, when there is nothing better to do, we may spare time to reason. Meanwhile we know that, here also, the romance is of more instant worth than the mere fact.

VIII

THE CONTEMPORARY

—This Disinterested Loan and Life Assurance is rather a capital concern, David.

—Capital, indeed!—in one sense.

—In the only important one—which is number one, David.

—What will be the paid up capital, according to your next prospectus?

—A figure of two, and as many oughts after it as the printer can get into the same line. . . .

—Well, upon my soul, you *are* a genius then.

—*Life and Adventures of Martin Chuzzlewit*

VIII

Which Concerns the Contemporary

SO it is in physical life that romance, when things go hopelessly wrong, without fail affords to mortals some makeshift whereby to preserve their self-esteem. . . . . And that brings me to another topic which has long been in the back of my mind, the other way in which romance may deal with actually present conditions, and make something more or less worthwhile of them, by transplantation in the field of literature. I have spoken, at some length, as to how creative writers came against their instincts to prevaricate about contemporary life, in concession to their patrons' mental indolence: and to the drawbacks and pitfalls of this proceeding I have alluded. Past doubt, it is infinitely safer to adhere to the Hellenic method of evoking protagonists worth noble handling from the bright mists of antiquity, wherethrough, as far as go existent proofs, men may in reality have moved "as they ought to be."

That, however, is very far from saying that
fine literature does not ever deal with the contemporaneous. Were there nothing else, nobody could advance such an insane statement in
English without forthwith incurring a liability
of having hurled at his head the Complete
Works of Charles Dickens. . . .

2

Yes, I know that, after so many others, to
speak of Dickens is to squander breath, and to
write of him is to waste good ink and paper. Indeed, for that matter, numerous cognoscenti
will assure you publishers do likewise when
they print his novels. For as literature, the
man's effusions are no longer taken very seriously by the lecturers before Women's Clubs.
The deuce of it is that, both colloquially and
mentally, he stays the ancestor of all of us: and,
like helpless victims of heredity, we must continue to repeat his phrases for lack of any adequate synonym, and our really popular fiction
seems condemned to haunt the levels of his
Christmas Carol philosophy.

Yet, as always, there is another side. "The
custom of ancestor worship," as Horace Cal-
verley somewhere observes, "has long been a

less potent fetish in the Kingdom of China than in the Republic of Letters." And, true enough, it was for a great while the wont of our general dunderheadedness to speak well of dead writers and decry all living authors, with the reassuring consciousness that thus no possible benefit could be incurred by anybody. There is even now a vast deal of respectability in Death: and he remains King-at-Arms in the literary world, wherein no title of nobility is assured until his seal has been affixed. "Death is the great assayer of the sterling ore of talent. At his touch the drossy particles fall off,—the irritable, the personal, the gross,—and mingle with the dust: the finer and more ethereal part mounts with the winged spirit to watch over our latest memory, and to protect our bones from insult. Death is a sort of natural canonization. It makes the meanest of us sacred: it installs the poet in his immortality, and lifts him to the skies." . . . So wrote Hazlitt in preparation for a volte-face dictated by that custom which makes bodily interment a condition of literary pre-eminence: and to the considerate even such fame as fills several pages in the encyclopædia, and a half-shelf in the library, seems purchased on quaint terms. . . .

But the present stays not always tamely subservient to the past; so that to become a "classic" is no assurance of perpetuity in the estate. Especially of late years has appraisal of our ancestors' ignorance in regard to aeroplanes and biology and suffrage, and motors and Prohibition and germs and the electric chair, begotten by analogy distrust of their clear-sightedness in all directions; and old literary values have borne up ill under their re-testing by the twentieth century, with that cocksureness peculiar to youngsters under twenty. The "personal reaction," in fine, has not been uniformly satisfactory; and as a consequence, pretty much everybody knows nowadays that the name of no novelist should be spoken with reverence if you are quite certain of its pronunciation; and that the correct verdict as to Dickens, at all events, should waver delicately between a yawn and a shrug.

When thus by so many persons no more seriously regarded than an obituary notice, the reputation of Dickens is in perilous plight. Confessed inability to read his novels is even regarded as incommunicably smacking of literary knowingness. His characters are mere personifications of certain qualities. His books present false pictures of life. And above all, he is that unforgivable monster, a Victorian. . . . So the tale goes, with blithe unconsciousness that these arraignments do but, in point of fact, sum up the reasons why his books will always delight the judicious.

Few persons not already under restraint would care to deny that Dickens unfailingly misrepresented the life he pretended to portray. To do this was, as I have shown, alike a requisite of art and of altruism: so the wise praise him therefor, knowing his merits to hinge far less on whether or no he has falsified the truth than on the delectable manner in which he has prevaricated. A novel, or indeed any work of art, is not intended to be a transcript from nature, *pace* all that cheerless reading-matter which our "realists" concoct for the agents of the Society for the Suppression of Vice. Truth, once hoisted from her well in primal nakedness, must like any other human failing be judiciously dressed in order to make an acceptable appearance in the library.

3

You might reasonably refrain from the noble pleasure of praising in discussion of a neighbor's intellectual clarity if he ranked diamonds and charcoal as of equivalent worth, on the ground that both are composed of carbon. Yet radically, such confusion would be no more egregious than that made by the creative writer who mingles the observed truth and his private inventions, with very little more discrimination than is exercised in such blending by a prosecuting attorney. "Realists" gravely contend that their books are true to what they see in life. It is consoling to deduce, from the comparative infrequency of suicide, that the majority of mankind view life otherwise. And yet, in such novels a naïve veracity is sometimes, beyond doubt, confusedly to be discerned among a multitude of other æsthetic offences. . . . For of course the mere fact of a thing's happening in nature does not affect in one way or another its right to happen in a novel: and to proclaim that "All this is truth" is really on a par with observing "All this is carbon." It should be the part of the creative writer skilfully to make a selection from the truths in regard to his subject, rather than to foist them wholesale into a transient grant of electrotype. Facts which are not to his purpose he is at liberty to omit, or to color, or at a pinch to deny. He must, in short, create unhampered, and shape his petty universe with the fine freedom of omnipotence. The truth therein must be whatever he wills to be the truth, and not a whit more or less: and his observation of actual life is an account on which he ought, at most, to draw small cheques to tide him over difficulties.

For the creative artist must remember that his book is structurally different from life, in that, were there nothing else, his book begins and ends at a definite point, whereas the canons of heredity and religion forbid us to believe that life can ever do anything of the sort. He must remember that his art traces in ancestry from the tribal huntsman telling tales about the cave-fire; and so, strives to emulate not human life, but human speech, with its natural elisions and falsifications. He must remember, too, that his one concern with the one all-prevalent truth in normal existence is jealously to exclude it from his book. . . . For "living" is to be conscious of an incessant series of less than momentary sensations, of about equal poignancy, for the most part, and of nearly equal unimportance. Art attempts to marshal the shambling procession into trimness, to usurp the rôle of memory and convention in assigning to some of these sensations an especial prominence, and, in the old phrase, to lend perspective to the forest we cannot see because of the trees. Art, as long ago observed my friend Mrs Kennaston, is an expurgated edition of nature: at art's touch, too, "the drossy particles fall off and mingle with the dust." And if Dickens has performed his expurgation so as to improve on the original, he is deserving of our gratitude.

4

To contest that Dickens has done this is futile. He has painted a clear-cut picture of the sort of world which he imagined he would like to inhabit. Questionless, his England is contiguous to Cloud-Cuckoo-Land, and his Anglo-Saxons intermarried with the Nepphelococcygians. There was never anyone in human flesh so meticulously enamored of *le mot juste* as Mr. Pecksniff, so prolific in weird modern instances as the Wellers *père et fils,* nor so felicitously garrulous as Mrs. Nickleby: yet this need not prevent their being the best of company. As Dickens has himself suggested—in his subtle depiction of Mrs. Harris, which is quite in the method of Henry James,—the non-existence of a person

detracts not at all from the merits of his or her
conversation. The features of these people are
over-emphasized, as are those of any actor when
he treads the stage, and the performance is all
the better for it. The characters of Mr. Theo-
dore Dreiser*, say, are more "true to life" (in
one of the many fields wherein candor is a ruinous virtue), and indeed can never be suppressed
into actual popularity. For few of us find living of such uniform excellence and nobility as
to endear a rehearsal thereof in the library: and
the more honest are willing to confess that our
average associates, to whom business and con-
sanguinity link us willy-nilly, are sufficiently
depressing in the flesh to induce a whole-hearted
avoidance of their counterparts in fiction. . . .

And when it comes actually to reading time-
hallowed books, however rarely such hard necessity arises in America, there is no doubting
that most of us prefer the grotesqueries of Mi-
cawber and Swiveller and Winkle to a nodding
intimacy with *Hamlet*, or to an out-and-out nap
over *Robinson Crusoe*, or to a vain dream of

*"Frankly we have little use for 'dunghill' literature, in
which branch of expression Dreiser is a past master. The flavor
throughout is hectic and unwholesome. It is not nice reading
for pure girls and high-minded women, nor yet for clean young
men."—*Evening Journal*, Richmond, Va.

having moistened the arid stretches of Clarissa Harlowe's correspondence with the tear of sensibility: and this does not prove that Dickens is superior in any way to Shakespeare or Defoe, or even Richardson, but simply that the majority of us find in Dickens less that is uncongenial. Mr. Bumble is not, upon the whole, a more masterfully portrayed character than Sir John Falstaff: but Mr. Bumble is more generally familiar, and, quite naturally, finds a far larger circle of sympathizers in his last stage,— which, as you may remember, was not to babble of green fields, but to be bullied by his wife.

And quaintly obsolete as it sounds, I am afraid there are still surviving a few of us old fogies who read Dickens with positive delight. We even hunt up an excuse or two in palliation. . . . For although the humor of Dickens may, as we are credibly informed, degenerate into buffoonery, it has a provoking habit of making people laugh. His pathos may, even to the extent of a stylistic scandal, be palpably forced, but from uncritical eyes it has drawn at least a Mediterranean of salt water. So we old fogies let detractors bay their uttermost: the moon has spots on it, but it remains a creditable luminary; and it is a pitiable form of myopia, say

we, that detects in a Belisarius only the holes
in his toga. Dickens very certainly has not depicted the real world in his writings, but therein
has made us free of an infinitely more pleasant
planet. He has endowed virtuous folk with a
preternatural power of coming out of trouble
with flying colors and congenial spouses, but
the most rigid moralist cannot well quarrel with
this equipoise to delinquent actuality. He may
even have made all good women short and
plump and fair, and all misguided females
haughty and tall and dark: yet every artist has
his mannerisms, and if Dickens chooses to make
the possession of desirable traits a question of
height and complexion, there too he improves
upon unscrupulous life, which in these matters
seems to have no principle whatever. Besides,
in Dickens-Land the residents are entitled to
their local customs and racial idiosyncrasies and
patois and peculiar social standards, just as
much as are the inhabitants of Austria and
Abyssinia and Arden. . . . Somewhat in this
fashion run the excuses of us frivolous old fogies, who are a little too old to regard men and
men's doings, even upon platforms, very seriously; and have lived through so many trials
and responsibilities that those which remain to

be encountered appear comparatively negligible, and much grave talk about them seems silly.

Of course, all this is "inartistic": it is the sort of conduct that grieved Flaubert, and continues to upset the sensibility of Mr. George Moore, as earnest-minded persons stand ready to protest in columns. For Dickens very often shocks the young by his lack of interest in sexual irregularities. Yet Dickens probably knew even more about novel-writing than do such sagacious folk as lecture and publish without general detection. No doubt he has his quirks and whimsies, which are common to the despot of any country: but we who love him are fain to believe that the king can do no wrong. . . . Perhaps that is begging the question: but then it is a question which should never have been raised. And if you can seriously debate "Is Dickens obsolete?" already, in so far as you are concerned, he is as obsolete as youth and April. For you have outgrown a novelist who "wallows naked in the pathetic," and is sometimes guilty of a vulgar sort of humor that makes people laugh, which, as we now know, is not the purpose of humor. . . . Indeed, to many persons not Torquemada or the Four

Evangelists can appear more remote in their way of thinking than does this novelist who shapes his plots with the long arm of coincidence, and never flies in the admiring foolish face of convention. For it depresses the conventionally "advanced" to see the man deal so liberally in cheerfulness: and they resent his happy-go-lucky methods of creating characters that seem more real to the judicious than the people we sit beside in streetcars, and (upon the whole) more vital and worthy of consideration than the folk who "cannot read Dickens." For Dickens regarded life from the viewpoint of a now unmodish optimism. . .

5

That reminds me of the remark by ordinary made as to Dickens which would be more patently absurd had not usage toned its lurid idiocy to the drab of commonplace. "No, I don't care for Dickens: I prefer Thackeray." To the philosophic mind it would seem equally sensible to decline to participate in a game of billiards on the ground that one was fond of herring. No considerate admirer of the dignified character of the ancient Britons will feel it a matter of absolute duty to paint himself blue.

Caractacus and Boadicea were no doubt as estimable in conduct as in costume they were frugal: the police anywhere may reasonably concede both circumstances without adding a permit to dispense with further patronage of the tailor: and very much as it is possible thus to render homage to moral excellence without the ascription of sartorial infallibility, so may you admire a manner of writing without belittling another man's way of clothing his thoughts. When an author offers us a good piece of work, it is folly to begrudge acknowledgement because another writer has done as well, or even better. Lovers of tolerably intelligent literature must take what they can come by, in a world which to them has never been over-generous.

But English-speaking races appear somehow called upon to uphold one of these writers at the expense of the other. Beside this disputation, the Hundred Years War was an affair of no moment. The combatants will have none of the watchman crying in our mental night, no matter how wisely Master Dogberry proclaims comparisons to be odorous: and there is only a small party of lawless renegades who think the verbose Sicilian in the right,—and so turn to the folk at Castlewood when Oliver Twist grows

rhetorical, and seek the company of Mrs. Gamp
when the moralizing becomes prolix in and
about Great Gaunt Street.

And it would be very pleasant, did time serve,
to prattle about Thackeray, too, and his equally
ingenious travesty of every day life for artistic
purposes. But Thackeray, when you come to
think of it, did his best work precisely when he
was not dealing with contemporary life, and
Esmond scores tremendously for the Hellenic
method. . . . Yet it must be noted that Thackeray also improved upon what was merely
plausible, and in very much the pertinacious
manner of Dickens, clung to a favorite *cliché*
which delights us in chief by reason of its antiquity. With Dickens there was always "the
comic countryman who overheard everything,"
and came forward toward the end of the twentieth monthly number to unmask the evil-doer:
in book after book this accident is unblushingly
tendered as a panacea for every human ill. With
Thackeray there was always the unsuspected
document lying perdu against its revealment or
destruction, as might best serve virtue, in the
twentieth monthly number,—whether as Lieu-
tenant Osborne's injudicious letter to Mrs.
Crawley, or as the will of Sophia Newcome or

of Lord Ringwood, or Henry Esmond's birth-certificate, or the Warringtons' deed to Castle-wood-in-Virginia. Thackeray is really not happy unless he has some such chirographic bombshell to explode in the last chapter. And in *Pendennis* you will find this omnipresent document assuming the droll form of the tattooing on Amory's arm: but here too Thackeray's obsessing *cliché* provides the happy winding-up of affairs. . . . No, I shall not insult you by pointing out that everybody's welfare does not thus quite invariably, and unanimously, pivot upon a bit of paper or an eavesdropper. But do you not perceive that these writers faithfully copied life in life's most important teaching, by inculcating that for persons who honor the æsthetic conventions of "good" and "evil" a happy ending impends and is inevitable, through however unlikely means? For the dynamic illusion of optimism is very thriftily fostered by romance in the wisest, and in the wise alone.

6

All in all, there is really no disputing that these two great optimists succeeded in writing delightfully about their contemporaries by the

258

simple device of not telling the truth. . . .
Probably few men of striking literary talent
have ever been so constituted as to be capable
of actually noticing what contemporary life was
like. The absent-mindedness of gifted writers
is, indeed, notorious: and it would seem to be
this habit of not closely observing their fellow
creatures which enables men of genius to write
about them so charmingly. At all events, once
the writing is adopted as a profession, the
author has definitely cut adrift from normal
life; and before long will forget its ordinary
course so completely that he may very well
come to misrepresent it in a masterpiece. . . .
Balzac, who was more profoundly painstaking
than most of us, adopted the plan of sleeping by
day, and writing throughout the night hours,
and of thus living for considerable periods
without seeing anyone save the domestic who
fetched the sustaining coffee: and Balzac's masterworks remain to prove this an excellent way
of writing really profound studies of contemporary life. It secures, to begin with, an abnormal viewpoint, concerning the need of which
I have spoken at sufficient length. And besides,
it is undeniable that a person who steadily per-
sisted in this ordering of his existence, as Bal-

zac did through some twenty-odd years, will not be creatively wind-bound by his knowledge of actualities and human nature as displayed therein: nor need I point out that the later volumes of the *Comédie Humaine* are concededly the best, improving as they did in ratio to Balzac's increasing forgetfulness of the truth about his subject. . . . Given the requisite genius, anyone of us may do well to follow his example. But the programme is arduous, and, first of all, you must be quite sure about the genius.

7

To divigate once more into egotism, I recall a book that was published some years ago with, I believe, quite gratifying misprision of the offence. This volume, at any rate, was handicapped by a preface in which this identical truism was cited,—that what mankind has generally agreed to accept as first-class art, in any of the varied forms of fictitious narrative, has never been a truthful reproduction of the artist's era. And the author, as I recall it, went on at some length to consider the futility of our "vital" novels, which affect to dispose of this or that problem of the day in the terms of "faithful realism." I was rather taken with the writer's exposition of what were more or less my own theories: and so, was no little interested, later, by the verdict thereanent of one of the few living novelists who, as a matter of any intelligent belief, has done work which will endure. . . . I think that verdict will repay quoting:

"Mr. —— is exactly right in intimating that the 'timely' is not generally the 'timeless.' And yet I can't help saying (I suppose, because 'no rogue e'er felt the halter draw with good opinion of the law') that I think it is a possible thing to be timely, if (and this is a very large 'if') the 'timely' is merely a method of showing the timeless. That is to say, if the reaction of the momentary phase of existence expresses some eternal phase of the human soul. *Uncle Tom's Cabin* was timely enough, but it was not its timeliness that made it survive: it was because, it seems to me, the book dealt with the ultimate passions of the human creature, with fear, and pity, and love. One could, I think, write a novel upon, say, the latest thing in automobiles, if the eccentricities of the self-starter or what-not simply ministered to some expression of that permanently 'vital' thing, the human heart. . . .

"I have twice ventured to be timely in fiction, and therefore I know how true is everything this Induction says about the 'vital' novel. And yet, 'Strike, but hear me!' Isn't it the trouble with Undine Spragg, for instance, that the 'vitalness' of the book is not founded upon truth, and therefore cannot possibly be permanent? It looks to me as if these people who tried to be 'vital' dealt only with facts: and the trouble with facts seems to be, that if one treats them out of relation to the rest of life, they become lies. Mrs. Wharton, for whose art I have the profoundest respect and admiration, offers us those horrid people in *The Custom of the Country,* with souls of a uniform tint of rather nasty and very dull blackness. Now, that is not true to life. There are black souls, God knows! But even in the blackest of them, I am convinced that the true artist will see some glimmering of white. To treat only the black, is indeed to be 'timely': it is to represent the moment and the phase, and not the everlasting emotions. . . .

"This Induction cuffs my ears so soundly, and so deservedly (apropos of my last book) that I have to ask for mercy, for myself and even for —— (whose books I have never read). Yet so

far as I am concerned, I did try to relate my
very timely subject to the timelessness of human passion, which seems to me like a living
root in the ground: the phases grow and blos-
som, like leaves and flowers, and drop into the
dust of time, but the root remains.''

8

Now that is a summing-up which everyone, remembering the writer's books, must perforce
view with reverence. It is the verdict of a person who speaks with authority. So I shall not
carp over an expression here and there, though
in regard to the permanent value of *Uncle
Tom's Cabin* the temptation is considerable to
speak daggers. . . . Instead, I thankfully accept the formula whereby the novel (and equally
the play or poem) of contemporary life may,
just possibly, become fine literature: if that
which is timely therein be made merely a
method of showing that which is timeless, and
if the momentary phase of existence be utilized
to express some eternal phase of the human
soul. Concerning the size of those ''ifs'' the
writer and I are in gratifying accord.

It comes almost to saying that the novel of
contemporary life, via the typewriter of the

serious artist, will return to the oldest of forms, and become more or less an allegory. . . . Indeed, this is inevitable. Book after book I find in the department-stores narrating how this or that particular person lived, wooed, married, labored, reared children, got into the divorce courts, made a fortune, acquired new opinions, or died. Often it is so convincingly set forth that the illusion of reality is produced: and for the instant the reader does believe that all this actually happened. But do you not see that to produce this illusion amounts to nothing æsthetically? I read of marriages and divorces and family squabbles and deaths and business-ventures by the dozen in the morning paper: and I believe that these too actually happened. Well, the "realistic" school of fiction, at its most ambitious reach of tedium, aims to convey the same impression, and nothing more. If "realism" be a form of art, the morning newspaper is a permanent contribution to literature. Undeniably, the "realist" invents his facts a trifle more daringly than the police reporter, and soars above mere veracity on an approximate level with the editorial writer: but not even on the plea of imagination can he claim to rank with the compilers of the weather predictions or of the society columns. . . . What John Jones may do or may refrain from doing really does not matter a button to anyone outside of his immediate circle of acquaintances: and the most faithful record of his actions, surely, cannot be made of enduring value to the world at large by the fact that they never took place and that Jones never existed. . . And yet, none the less, this novel of contemporary life may be informed by art if, through some occult magic, the tale becomes a symbol: and if, however dimly, we comprehend that we are not reading merely about "John Jones, aged 26, who gave his address as 187 West Avenue," but about humanity,—and about the strivings of that ape reft of his tail, and grown rusty at climbing, who yet, however dimly, feels himself to be a symbol, and the frail representative of Omnipotence in a place that is not home; and so strives blunderingly, from mystery to mystery, with pathetic makeshifts, not understanding anything, greedy in all desires, and honeycombed with poltroonery, and yet ready to give all, and to die fighting, for the sake of that undemonstrable idea. If, in short, the chronicle becomes a symbol of that which is really integral to human existence, in a sense to which motor cars and marriage licenses and

265

even joys and miseries appear as extraneous things,—why, then and then only, this tale of our contemporaries shifts incommunicably to fine art. . . .

I wonder if you are familiar with that uncanny genius whom the London directory prosaically lists as Arthur Machen? If so, you may remember that in his maddening volume *Hieroglyphics* Mr. Machen circumvolantly approaches to the doctrine I have just voiced—that all enduring art must be an allegory. No doubt, he does not word this axiom quite explicitly: but then Mr. Machen very rarely expresses outright that which his wizardry suggests. And it is perhaps on account of this rash reliance upon intelligence and imagination, as being at all ordinary human traits, that Mr. Machen has failed to appeal as instantly as, we will say, Mr. Robert W. Chambers* appeals to

*A novelist of the day, appropriately commemorated by Captain Rupert Hughes (another writer of fiction) in the *Cosmopolitan Magazine*, for June, 1918. "Mr. Chambers . . . does not run about the world shaking his fist at the sky or spitting in other people's faces. . . . There is an eternal summer in his heart. The world is his rose garden." Mr. Chambers, according to the same authority, has written "masterpieces," "triumphs of art," "superb fantasy," "thrilling drama," etc., etc., dealing for the most part with "well-groomed men and women in their stately homes."

those immaculate and terrible ladies who languidly vend books in our department stores, and with Olympian unconcern confer success upon reading-matter by "recommending" it. . . But here in a secluded library is no place to speak of the thirty years' neglect that has been accorded Mr. Arthur Machen: it is the sort of crime that ought to be discussed in the Biblical manner, from the house-top. . . And, besides, I am digressing.

Art, then, must deal with contemporary life by means of symbols. Never for a moment will art in dealing with the actual life about us restrict its concern to John Jones, as a person, any more than, as I have suggested, does the art of the Bible ever pivot upon Abraham or Solomon as individual persons. . . It was perhaps intuitively that Dickens—very briefly to revert to him,—obeyed this necessity, but he regarded it, none the less: and so you will find, even to-day, the more hopelessly obtuse among us deprecating that his characters are "personifications of certain qualities". . . And of course it is idle to argue with folk who were mentally stillborn and grotesquely flourish the corpse as something of which to be proud. They boggle less over Thackeray, who explains

267

the meaning of his symbols over and over again, with delightfully indefensible side-taking and moralizing, until even dullards comprehend what he is writing about. . .

Art, I repeat, must deal with contemporary life by means of symbols. And the creative writer should handle facts religiously, in that particular mood of piety which holds that incomplete accord with a creator's will is irreligious. . . Facts must be kept in their proper place, outside of which they lose veracity.

9

To go back a little—"the trouble with facts seems to be, that if one treats them out of relation to the rest of life, they become lies." . . There in brief you have the damnatory frailty of "realistic" novels, which endeavor to show our actual existence from a viewpoint wherefrom no human being ever saw it. For literature—need I repeat it?—should be true to life: and the serious artist will not attempt to present the facts about his contemporaries as these facts really are, since that is precisely the one indiscretion which life never perpetrates. In literature facts should not be handled intelligently, for the simple reason that in living no fact or happening reveals itself directly to man's intelligence; but is apprehended as an emotion, which the sustainer's prejudices color with some freedom. Thus, were you to hear of your wife's sudden death it would come to you not, I hope, as an interesting fact, but as a grief: and with the advent of your first-born you are conscious not at all of the newcomer's ugliness and untoothed imbecility—which are the undeniable facts,—but gratefully receive a priceless joy. All the important happenings of life, indeed, present themselves as emotions that are prodigally conformed by what our desires are willing to admit: it is indisputable, for instance, that a quite different account from any which we now possess of the Betrayal and Crucifixion would have been rendered, and honestly believed in, by the mother of Judas. Even life's trivialities arrive in the livery of emotion: to receive a letter is either a pleasure or a nuisance, and what there is for dinner appreciably affects the spirit-level. We, in fine, thus fritter through existence without ever encountering any facts as they actually are: for in life no fact is received as truth until the percipient has conformed and colored it to suit his preferences: and in this also literature should be true to life. . .

Then, too, to make a complete and fair-minded analysis of any human being, as "realists" affect to do, is forthwith to avoid any conceivable viewpoint: since our acquaintances, to whom alone we are impartial, we do not take the trouble to analyze, and to our intimates, with whom alone we are familiar, we can by no possibility remain impartial. You would thus no more think of inquiring into your grocer's reasons for turning Methodist than of abhorring your brother because he happened to have murdered somebody. . . The artist, as has been said, requires a viewpoint that is abnormal: but he can make no very profitable use of one which does not exist. That much cried-up volume, *Madame Bovary,* for example, is doubtless a painstaking delineation of a sort of a something, which nobody can take oath to be a woman. For, inasmuch as this deplorable Emma is studied with an intimacy and an aloofness of feeling which in human life cannot coëxist in an observer, you have no data whereby to judge the portrait's verisimilitude. It may resemble a certain woman seen from that especial standpoint: but then nobody ever saw a real woman from that standpoint. The thing may well be like a village doctor's wife when thus regarded: yet so far as positive knowledge goes, it may be even more like a dromedary viewed from the North Pole: for Flaubert is refining phrases about a collocation outside of human experience. . . And all the other "realistic" writers, who thus set forth to record intelligently the facts of cotemporaneous existence, are introducing facts to the reader's perception after a fashion for which life affords no parallel. And so their facts becomes lies, because "realism" as a literary method is fundamentally untrue to life; and by attempting to exhibit our contemporaries as being precisely what they are, does but very ill compare with actual life, which is far more charitable.

10

Really there should be no trifling with facts. For always the ever-present danger exists that, in treating of the life immediately about him, even the unobservant literary genius may notice that this life for the most part consists of ugly and stupid persons doing foolish things, and will take a despondent view of the probable outcome. . . Not everyone of us, whatever our

private belief, writes quite as understandingly
as Shakespeare: and even he, in addition to the
peccadilloes previously noted, was very guilty
of *Timon* and of *Troilus and Cressida.* But
Shakespeare, being what he was, went beyond
all that, and came at last to the astounding
"romantic" plays written after his retirement
to Stratford. . . There is strong meat in their
serene indifference to moral indignation. Le-
ontes and Iachimo and Antonio of Milan are
every whit as evil as Shylock and Iago: but the
dramatist is not at pains to invent any punishment for the latelier-begotten scoundrels; for to
enwidened vision it has become doubtful if the
full reach of human wickedness can, after all,
amount to very much. . .

And so this poet is reputed to have said: "I
never knew a wicked person. I question if anybody ever did. Undoubtedly, short-sighted
people exist who have floundered into ill-doing:
but it proves always to have been on account
of either cowardice or folly, and never because
of malevolence; and in consequence, their sorry
pickle should demand commiseration far more
loudly than our blame. In short, I find humanity to be both a weaker and a better-mean-
ing race than I had suspected. . . I grant the

272

world to be composed of muck and sunshine intermingled: but, upon the whole, I find the sunshine more pleasant to look at. . . And I hold that all human imbroglios, in some irrational and quite incomprehensible fashion, will be straightened to our satisfaction. . . Meanwhile this universe of ours, and, reverently speaking, the Maker of this universe as well, is under no actual bond to be intelligible in dealing with us.''

That, too, is the verdict of a person who knows what he is talking about. It is the anodyne, however variously labeled, of every candid philosopher in putting up with those innumerable, continuous, small, nagging and inescapable annoyances which compound his life as a human being: and it serves as a cordial to sustain him in almost all his dealings with his contemporaries. Equally it is a creed to which the literary artist, also, must cling fast, yet not too desperately, in dealing with his contemporaries. . . It is the utterance of a man who, to revert to the old phrase, ''has encountered Pan,'' and yet has perceived, too, that in everything romance, to serve the unforeseeable purpose of the demiurge, begets and nourishes the dynamic illusion of optimism. And he knows, he knows not how, that the demiurgic spirit of romance strives not without discernment toward noble ends. Thus it is alone that, in defiance of the perturbing spectacle of man's futility and insignificance, as the passing skin-trouble of an unimportant planet, he can still foster hope and urbanity and all the other gallant virtues, serenely knowing all the while that if he builds without any firm foundation his feat is but the more creditable.

IX
THE ARBITERS

She stood before him in all the beautiful strength of her young womanhood.

He was really a fine looking young man with the appearance of being exceptionally well-bred and well-kept. Indeed the most casual of observers would not have hesitated to pronounce him a thoroughbred and a good individual of the best type that the race has produced. . . .

—Barbara, he cried, don't you *know* that I love you? . . . Don't you know that nothing else matters? Your desert has taught me many things, dear, but nothing so great as this—that I want you and that nothing else matters. I want you for my wife.

—*The Winning of Barbara Worth*

IX

Which Defers to the Arbiters

T O attain the ends I have indicated may, then, be taken as the peculiar duty of the literary artist who is reduced to writing about his contemporaries. . . Put to a jury of average discrimination, however, the question, what is the first requirement of a novelist? would probably result in a hung verdict. The less prosaic would answer "A publisher," and the ten dullards would prattle of "original ideas" quite as though they discoursed of possibilities. And the whole dozen would be right enough: for the publisher is really indispensable, whereas from the point of view of commerce—and really æsthetics is in no wise concerned,—our modern novel is nothing if it have not some superficial novelty, to arrest the roving and languid interest with which all people (turned pessimists by experience) hear about new fiction. . . Yet the humane laws of the land compel no man to read another's book. Emboldened by this fact, the general reader demands, with his visage too betraying such æsthetic zeal as may fairly be described as characteristic:—

"Interest me, against my natural inclinations, in your printed nonsense, and I will buy such novels of yours as I cannot borrow. I do not at all go in for reading and that sort of thing, when I can find anything else to do: but once in a while there is a vacant half-hour I have to get rid of somehow. At such times I am willing to put you on an equal footing with the evening paper and the cinematograph, since I reserve the right to quit any one of you the moment I find the entertainment distasteful. So, go ahead now with your fooleries and remember I am here to be shocked or elevated or instructed or harrowed or otherwise taken out of myself: and let us have no 'literary' nonsense, because I resent the impudence of people who allude to matters that I do not understand."

It seems little enough to ask in return for a whole ten per cent commission on a book that costs the general reader, very often, as much as his cravat. Still, it is a mercantile offer, which every true artist would meet with contempt if only it were possible to discharge the monthly accounts with the same coinage. But, unfortunately, most books are less a question of art than of bread and butter. The average fiction-writer, at all events, can afford to look down upon the public only, as the acrobat looks down upon the tight-rope, to ascertain whither it leads, and to make sure that it will support him. . .

Nor is it impeccable etiquette to blow one's own trumpet: yet each musician undoubtedly makes the most noise with his own instrument. So in the Vanity Fair of Current Letters every tradesman makes bold to commend his especial wares. . . The attractions are many and various. Here is Mr. Booth Tarkington dispensing, past doubt, the best confectionery in the market. At the familiar stand Mr. W. D. Howells is still making tintypes, and guaranteeing a perfect likeness. Mr. Bernard Shaw, of course, is in charge of that intriguing exhibition, the Crazy House, where everything is exhibited upside down: and in the fortune-teller's tent, recently vacated by Mr. H. G. Wells, is prophesying this week I forget precisely who. Yonder row of pavilions is devoted to a display of precocious orphans, and you are warned not to enter with less than two pocket handkerchiefs. Those who are interested by the sport of shying missiles at inkily colored persons can be diverted, to your left, at any number of stalls, conducted by such dissimilar folk as ambassadors, newspaper correspondents, retired spies, and ex-governesses to the nobility. Over yonder a very considerable section of the fair-grounds is set apart for the performances commended by Colonel Roosevelt. And of course there are any number of tents with flamboyant placards stating that the exhibit within concerns the highest and most exclusive society, and narrowly escaped being forbidden by the police. . . It is a motley bazaar, and to make any choice therein cannot but puzzle the visitor with limited resources for his fairing.

Now all this is very new and original indeed, and the general reader ought to be satisfied. For it is at his demand the age thus pullulates with reading-matter for the non-literary. Still, all progress brings its attendant problems: and in this case one honestly wonders what is to become of our old literary masterpieces, now that people decline to read them. For there can be no earthly doubt that to a steadily augmenting majority the time-honored bulk of English literature means only a forgotten "course" at school or college, along with the calculus and botany and other matters there is no longer any need to worry over, until it comes to helping the children with their lessons. . .

Nor was this state of affairs avoidable. In order to appreciate the productions of a departed age, it is necessary to be familiar with the era: and time has added ruthlessly, no less to the ranks of literary masterpieces, than to the number of requisite viewpoints. There is really no end of actual drudgery entailed nowadays in becoming tolerably conversant with English literature, and comprehending, if but more or less, what the authors are about. And when it comes to consideration of their interplay on one another, and their derivative sources, and their borrowings from other literatures—all which are quite essential studies if we are to 'read with comprehension,—the prospect broadens out into little better than a lifetime of penal servitude. It is a vista before which the student quails, and the better-balanced general public shrugs and turns its back.

As a case in point, one may well consider that especial glory of English letters, the much-vaunted plays of the Elizabethan and Jacobean dramatists, which justly rank so high in literature that few can endure the altitude. Here for the asking is, in cold earnest, "the greatest part of the greatest period of the greatest literature of the world": and to extol this quite priceless literary heritage of ours as animated, impassioned, brilliant and inimitable, would be to deal in text-book truisms; but to describe it as generally pleasant reading would be an absurdity. To the most of us such portions as we can understand at all sound uncommonly like nonsense: and throughout, the flavor of unreality in these dramas is even stronger than their depressing odor of antiquity. Our instinctive attitude toward them becomes much the same as that of Tom Tulliver toward the Latin language. Yet managers once with perfect justice classed these plays as "light popular stuff," and the jokes we puzzle out with the aid of commentaries and foot-notes were put in for the especial benefit of the uneducated. . . Then there is *The Spectator*, which time has transmuted from a popular periodical into a pest. And all the productions of Mrs. Aphra Behn, the seventeenth century Elinor Glyn, and of Samuel Richardson, who was the Florence Barclay of his day,—these too assist to prompt avoidance of the well selected library.* . .

<h2 style="text-align:center">2</h2>

For time has erected barriers more or less serious before all the "popular" reading-matter of yester-year. From this side of the fence, the prospect seems attractive enough, and for Cervantes, let us say, nearly everybody has a civil superlative. . . But the actual climbing of the palings, to the extent of reading famous books, instead of the books about them, provokes inevitable disillusion. The moon is beyond question interesting when glanced at through a moderate sized telescope, but actually to sojourn on its surface might prove insufferably tedious. . . Thus every self-respecting person will assure you, with whatever pronunciatory divergence, that Don Quixote is one of the great characters of fiction: and past doubt the ingenious gentleman of La Mancha is a delightful companion, in anticipation. What could be more diverting than the adven-

*Charteris likens Richardson and Mrs. Behn to writers contemporary with Charteris. "Mrs. Glyn possesses a brilliant intellect, which she uses to probe unsparingly into the human soul." - - *Cosmopolitan Magazine* for September 1918. Mrs. Barclay also had admirers.

ture of Mambrino's helmet, and that perfectly killing affair of the windmills? and where will you find nowadays such wonderful character-drawing as in Sancho Panza? You thrill to the notion of a jaunt through old-world Spain in company with these two immortal types of humanity, concerning whom, as you glowingly remember, it has been strikingly observed by Somebody-or-other that such-and-such is the case. . . So you begin the book, in an atmosphere of genial goodfellowship, which vanishes long before the end of the fourth chapter. For it is an unfortunate fact that, so far as most of us are concerned, the essayists have written much more entertainingly about Don Quixote than Cervantes ever did. And when you fairmindedly consider that noble structure which commentators and occasional writers have erected with the works of Rabelais as foundation, you will hardly contend that the most attractive portion of the building is the cellar. . .

Yet, by the pertinacious, these time-raised barriers are surmountable: and once over, there is pleasant enough adventuring to be found, in and about the domains that are being held in trust for posterity. The surroundings are, indeed, rather different from what might be expected. Some monuments of genius, which from a distance seemed most imposing, reveal to closer inspection a great deal of clumsy joiner's-work: and others turn out to be mere piles of odds and ends. Posterity appears to be as much by way of falling heir to the slap-dash and the incidental work as to inheriting that which was aspiringly put together for her edification. . . Indeed, a many ambitious epistles especially designed for posterity's perusal have gone astray in transit, and any number of personal communications, addressed elsewhere and written with never a thought of her, have fallen by pure luck into the hands of her trustees, to be ranked among her most amiable treasures. . .

There was one John Dryden, for example, who was incessantly plaguing himself about the debatable tastes of unborn readers: tragedies, comedies, satires, pastorals, elegies, and other dignified displayals of his genius were despatched to posterity every year. There lived coetaneously, in the same city, a government official of more or less importance, a secretary of the Admiralty, who in hours of leisure jotted down a diary for his own amusement. Dryden was a fine poet, and wears morocco worthily:

there is perhaps no surer test of culture than an ability to read *The Conquest of Granada* with enjoyment. Still, nobody pretends it is as pleasant to yawn over *The Spanish Friar* and *Sir Martin Mar-all* as to listen to Mr. Pepys's quarrels with his wife ("poor wretch!"), observe the glowworms with Mrs. Turner, and witness the execution of Major Harrison,—who, having been hanged, drawn and quartered, with really deathless optimism, "looked as cheerful as any man could do in that condition." Shall we glance over *The Hind and the Panther* and *Absalom and Achitophel,* those eminently meritorious productions, or shall we follow the secretary from the House to Hercules-pillars?—or to a stolen tête-à-tête with Mrs. Knipp, or to church, or to the Duke's theater, or to an hour's practise on the flute, or to reflective contemplation of Saturn through a twelve foot glass, and "so to bed"? There is only one answer for any right-minded man. . . The reading public, of course, is not right-minded. This is not to say, indeed, that the general public prefers Dryden to Pepys: to the contrary, it enrolls both, with most of our elder writers, in the ranks of the Great Unread. . .

3

As we have seen, then, among the important questions of our time (as public speakers pleasingly put it) is the problem: what can be done toward educating the taste of the general reading public. And the answer, of course, is bother the general public! It reads what it chooses, has always done so, and will in all probability continue to do so indefinitely. The general public to-day, as always, has no concern with literature, which, as previously pointed out, is a starveling cult kept alive by the "literary". And *vice versa,* we have seen too that when literature at all considers the taste of the general public and the trend of the writer's time, the result may range anywhere between the "comedy" of Marlowe and the "sentiment" of Sheridan, over an awe-inspiring field of enormities. . . Meanwhile the general public patronizes Mr. Winston Churchill,* and Mrs. Florence Barclay, and Mr. Sydnor Harrison, and Mr. Harold Bell Wright, through just that sober enjoyment of being told over and over again what nobody thinks of denying which

*Charteris here enumerates a few writers—all novelists,— who were in vogue at the time he spoke.

weekly draws it churchward. It regales itself with Sir Conan Doyle, and Mr. R. W. Chambers, and Mr. Phillips Oppenheim, and Sir Hall Caine, on much the principle that it eats popcorn and peanuts, less from any especial delight in the diet than from an impulse to get to the bottom of the bag. And lastly, and above all, the general public quite sincerely enjoys reading any book, of any kind, that is being read by the public generally, through much that herd instinct for doing what everybody else is doing, which exalts sane women upon three-inch heels, and attaches buttons to the sleeves and coat-tails of presumably intelligent men. So that in reading the general public is not influenced by its literary taste, but by qualities less esoteric.

This, then, is the conclusion of the matter: that, as literature goes, the verdict, or rather the aversion, of the reading public may be disregarded. For literature is a cult kept alive by the "literary." And the fact that the general public no longer reads time-hallowed books has really no more to do with literature than have the books it actually does read. Sometimes, for one reason or another, the general public talks about, and perhaps reads, a quite excellent

288

piece of writing. And were there a company that insured the lives of books—though probably no author, even as beneficiary, would ever admit that any seeming demise among his brain-children amounted to more than catalepsy,—it is gratifying to-day to note the number of apparently good "risks" in America. For instance, this desiderated company would beyond doubt insure at a quite moderate premium the ink and paper offspring of Mr. Joseph Hergesheimer: and would not the terms offered Mr. Booth Tarkington (to whom I shall presently recur in exasperated admiration) be made unusually "attractive"?

One is here tempted to enumerate at least a corporal's guard of promising living candidates for the "literary themes" of unbuilded class-rooms; and is deterred by the reflection that all such lists can only be dictated by prejudice and compiled by self conceit. Setting aside his own books, no living author could very confidently go on record as to what Arks are just now discernible in the deluge of current fiction, because in such matters any honest prophecy is a vain thing. Posterity amasses its literary heirlooms by no known standard: and when it comes to predicting which books will live, and which are passing into oblivion via tremendous popularity, no person, and no class of persons, is competent to say what trait it is that, somehow, gives a book vitality.

4

Publishers, upon their purely commercial plane, appear agreed that the miracle is performed, very much as vitality was conferred on Adam, by word of mouth. When readers commend a novel to their acquaintances, so rumor runs in editorial fastnesses, the book's future is assured. "Now, that's what I call a pretty good story," says So-and-so: and Such-an-one receives the dictum with a confidence he would never accord the verdict of a professional reviewer, whose approval is vexatiously apt sometimes to be based upon the volume's merits as a piece of literature. . .

Now the age-old sneer against professional reviewers as being unsuccessful authors, who have acquired, by virtue of demonstrating their innate incapacity to write readable books, a glib ability to instruct others in that art, is in most cases pointless. Usually, indeed, it is the other way around: and one might enumerate any number of present-day novelists whom the decade has seen like stars start from their critical spheres. Even were the old slur always barbed with veracity, however, its repetition need gall nobody. For the practising reviewer of current reading-matter has, of course, in the exercise of his trade no more concern with literary values than has the shoemaker or the magazine-editor or the blacksmith in the pursuit of their several vocations. This rule, like every general rule, is attested by its exception, to-day delightfully incarnate in the always exceptional Mr. H. L. Mencken,—who illicitly begets new ideas upon ancient culture, and, like an erratic chemist, uses as an acid to test contemporary humbug such erudition as staider critics employ as oxygen for the moribund in tooled calf. No less, this rule applies to normal persons: and a conscientious newspaper critic ought not to read much of anything. The books he is condemned to review are naturally out of the question, were it but that his contribution toward his family's support depends upon retention of his mental health: whereas familiarity with what mankind has in the main agreed to accept as great literature will handicap him without fail, and ultimately will lessen the market-value of his paragraphs, by mitigating the infallibility of his tone.

291

For, no one who cared cordially for literature has ever been a competent critic of literature. To the mental eye examples throng with the reputed contiguity of leaves in Vallambrosa. The men and women who made our enduring books have by ordinary been mistaken in appraising the relative importance of what they themselves had written, and almost every one of them has tended to estimate as a feather in his cap what posterity has found a thorn in the side. But in weighing the value of one another's productions, distinguished authors have been wrong without fail. You must permit me a few pedantic citations of appalling instances. . . Voltaire considered Shakespeare a barbarian, and said so without scruple or any great harm. Madame de Staël complained of the "commonness" of Jane Austen's novels, of which the merits were equally imperceptible to Charlotte Brontë. Wordsworth termed *Candide* "the dull product of a scoffer's pen," to the astonishment of many who would otherwise have considered the author of *Peter Bell* an authority on dullness. Coleridge discovered nothing very remarkable in Gray. Southey complained that the *Essays of Elia* were lacking in sound religious feeling, and pronounced *The Ancient*

Mariner "the clumsiest attempt at German sublimity I ever saw." Keats (at whom Byron sneered) found in the writers of the Augustan age of England only a school of dolts that mistook a rocking-horse for Pegasus: and his especial indignation against their precentor, Boileau, is not unnatural, in view of the latter's plagiarism of his *"rien n'est beau que le vrai"* from Keats's most often quoted line,—made with low cunning so many years before the birth of Keats. . . Then Thackeray has left it on record that either he or Dickens understood nothing about novel-writing: and Dickens agreed with him, as posterity on this particular point has done with neither. For the rest, Swinburne was at small pains to conceal his real opinion of Tennyson, and Dr. Johnson considered whipping the proper reward of anyone who would read twice a poem of Milton's. . . One might cite other instances, but the mad tale would stretch to the crack of doom. Its unavoidable moral would seem to be that this word-of-mouth criticism by concededly incompetent people, through which books "sell," is in comparison quite competent criticism.

5

Thus to repeat, at this late day, the sayings

of obsolete persons who wrote novels in monthly numbers and poems in metrical verse, may no doubt appear pedantic: but even so, these dire examples prove pretty plainly that you cannot trust a man who has read much, to select your reading-matter. Literature is precisely the one thing which cannot be correctly judged from literary standpoints. We come thus to the gist of the whole matter,—that by each of us whatever he reads or finds unreadable must be appraised independently. One may merely say—with reverent acknowledgment that the verdict has no jurisdiction in remoter libraries,—whether or not one likes the book. After all, that is the only thing about the volume which matters. If a book gives pleasure, then, in so far as the reader is concerned, it is a praiseworthy book. Wiser men may go farther, and fare proverbially, by explaining how and why it pleases: as in like manner, a stationer might fix the precise value of its paper per ream. But none of these may settle the sole question in which any reader can take rational interest,—which is, whether or not he likes the book. Everybody must decide that matter for himself: and no critic can help in the decision, from Mr. Chesterton of *The Illustrated London*

News to Job of Uz, who first of all people betrayed the characteristics of a born reviewer, by his disparaging *résumé* of the universe and his unconcealed desire to have his enemy write a book.

6

By each of us whatever he reads must be appraised independently. The general reading public, without knowing it, has grasped, and practises, this great fundamental principle of criticism; which yet remains unapprehended by far more cultured persons, to their not inconsiderable annoyance. Thus, more extensive recognition of this principle would do away with at least one gigantic humbug that continually teases most Americans,—say, all those persons of sufficient social rank to take interest in the current price of gasoline,—who go enshackled by the necessity of having, or pretending to have, some knowledge of, and even a liking for, the books generally accepted to constitute the main glories of literature. It would put a stop to much pernicious platitudinizing as to the Hundred Best Books and Five-Foot Shelves to contain them, by pedagogues whose first requirement is that an author be no longer alive, and by æsthetes who merely demand that he abstain from liveliness. For no book could then in itself be "best" or even "good": its merits would confessedly depend on who was reading it. Viewed from an ethical standpoint alone, the incurrent benefits of this understanding would be invaluable. We would be relieved from the compulsion of seeming to admire *The Faëry Queen;* we need not, even in writing essays, refer knowingly to Richardson with an air of having read his novels; and if we found Miss Corelli* a more congenial companion than Shakespeare,—nor can there be any possible doubt as to with which of these twain the majority of us have most in common,—we could unhesitatingly say so. The morality of book-purchasers would be raised, and reading would become to people of education a positive pleasure. Nowadays it is not entirely all cakes and ale: for if one reads with any higher quest than pastime, misguided self-respect will presently be snaring the unwary into great company. The genius of Æschylos and Virgil and Dante, and

*A novelist of the day. "Miss Corelli's stories . . . are much more than novels that are read and are forgotten; they contain sound philosophy; they stimulate the mind; they educate; they are permanent."—*Hearst's Magazine,* September, 1917.

such folk, is so stupendous that it can be admired from a considerable distance. Very few of us are fit to associate with these superior beings, or with the attempt, to be quite at ease in Sion. We are, when all is said, perturbed before such high-strung utterance, and reflect that sensible people take existence more easily. Sublime, immortal, and after that out of all whooping, we may willingly and honestly acclaim these bards, without of necessity enjoying their books. So we admire, more or less whole-heartedly: and when it comes to reading, pick up the handiest new popular novel, with rather less optimism than when, with similar intent, we enter into conversation with strangers on a railway journey, in order to kill off a vacant half-hour.

And it is highly improbable that you or I will live to see a termination of this lying about literature,—which is, to all appearance, as instinctive as the dislike every healthy boy entertains toward the Bible. It may happen, indeed, that the day will never dawn wherein honest persons may without incurring the suspicion of illiteracy or posturing admit the longwinded drivel of *The Life and Strange Surprising Adventures of Robinson Crusoe of York, Mariner,*

to be commensurate with the title; and point
out that the erotic misdemeanors of Tom Jones
are, after all, too few and too inadequately de-
tailed to prevent his biography being tiresome.
These books, with many others, retain a sort of
barnacle-grasp on literature, long after loss of
vitality. And they will never be out of print,
of course, in view of the delightful cycle of
romance which centres about each, in the form
of essays on its author's life and genius.

Yet always the consoling thought remains
that, while cowardice may force us to speak reverently of famous books, no police-regulation
has ever dared to meddle with hypocrisy. And
the humane laws of the land compel no man to
read another's books. . .

7

Meanwhile illiteracy is becoming as rare as
all the other characteristics of the Golden Age.
. . And among the multifarious results of universal education, the candid philosopher will
not fail to admire a curious by-product of teaching everybody to read (in disregard of most
persons' really cultivable powers), in the modern American novel of commerce, thriving

everywhere by virtue of the truism that unto each his like seems good. . .

That venerable adage may be taken as the not very startling explanation of the appeal of every really popular novel nowadays. It is about the sort of book its average reader would have written were he, too, stung by the gadfly of self-expression. It is a book which respects its average reader's limitations, for the excellent reason that the author shares them. It is a book which flatters its readers' pet delusions, because the author also honestly believes these rank among the eternal verities. And above all, of course, it is a book which pictures humanity as a superhuman race, who are leading purposeful lives, and have always in view some clearly apprehended aim, whether it be a lady's happiness or the will of somebody's uncle. For that each of us is consciously attempting to get something perfectly definite out of existence, is the average man's most jealously preserved belief, if only because it is the most difficult to preserve. So that the reward for manufacturing reading-matter of this sort is very properly munificent, since the precise intellectual deficiencies necessary thereto must be congenital, and certainly cannot be acquired by taking thought.

Books fulfilling these general requirements fall into innumerable sub-divisions, which might be not unprofitably catalogued by students of arrested development. Meanwhile Mr. Winston Churchill* has his clientèle, who stand ready to purchase all further simply-worded explanations of the obvious. Here and there some of the very faithful admirers of Mr. Sydnor Harrison* are prepared to make affidavit they read all of *V V's Eyes,* as this writer rather quaintly christened the best of his books. Mr. R. W. Chambers,* too, retains his eminently Cosmopolitan audience to the utmost reach of the rural delivery routes: and thousands will never think of refraining from the meed of a melodious tear so long as Mrs. Florence Barclay* continues to publish woes untold. And Mr. Booth Tarkington, also, is a very popular novelist. . . But that I take to be one of the most tragic items in all the long list of misfortunes which have befallen American literature. It is a fact that merits its threnody, since the loss of an artist demands lamentation, even when he commits suicide.

*Compare page 287.

8

For if, as Stevenson declared, the fairies were tipsy at Mr. Kipling's christening, at Mr. Tarkington's they must have been in the last stage of maudlin generosity. Poetic insight they gave him; and the knack of story building; and all their own authentic elfin liveliness of fancy; and actually perceptive eyes, by virtue of which his more truly Tarkingtonian pages are enriched with countless happy little miracles of observation; and the dramatic gift, of contriving and causing to move convincingly a wide variety of puppets in nothing resembling the puppet-master; and the not uncommon desire to "write," with just enough deficiency in common-sense to make him willing to put up with the laboriousness of writing fairly well. In fine, there is hardly one natural endowment requisite to grace in a creative author that was omitted by these inebriated fairies. And to all this Mr. Tarkington has since added, through lonesome and grinding toil, an astounding proficiency at the indoor sport of adroit verbal expression. No living manipulator of English employs the contents of his dictionary more artfully or, in the general hackneyed and misleading phrase, has a better "style."

No less, for many years Mr. Tarkington has been writing "best-sellers," varied every once in a while by something that was a "best-seller" in nature rather than performance. His progress has been from the position of a formidable rival of the late Mr. Charles Major (not very long ago the world-famous author of a story entitled *When Knighthood Was in Flower*) to the point of figuring prominently in *The Saturday Evening Post.** So that, upon the whole, one wonders if ere this the fairies have not humored their protégé yet further, by becoming Prohibitionists.[2]

Mr. Tarkington has published nothing that does not make very "pleasant" reading. He has in fact re-written the quaint legend, that virtue and honest worth must rise inevitably to be the target both of rice-throwing and of respectful consideration by the bank cashier, as

*A widely circulated advertising medium which printed considerable fiction; published in Philadelphia.

[2]Sectarians of the period, who upheld the tenets of Mohammed as opposed to those of Christ in the matter of beverages; and made of dietary preferences a national issue, in imitation of the wars of Lilliput and Blefescu over the preferable manner of eating eggs. Charteris frequently mentions this heresy.

indefatigably as human optimism and the endurance of the human wrist would reasonably permit. For the rest, his plots are the sort of thing that makes criticism seem cruel. His ventriloquism is startling in its excellence; but his marionettes, under the most life-like of exteriors, have either hearts of gold or entrails of sawdust; there is no medium: and as touches their behavior, all the Tarkingtonian puppets "form themselves" after the example of the not unfamous young person who had a curl in the middle of her forehead. And Mr. Tarkington's auctorial philosophy was summed up long ago, in *The Gentleman from Indiana.* "Look," said Helen. "Aren't they good dear people?" —"The beautiful people!" he answered.

Now this, precisely this, Mr. Tarkington has been answering ever since to every riddle in life. To-day he is still murmuring, for publication, "The good dear people, the beautiful people!"—who, according to his very latest bulletin at the moment I speak, are presently to be awarded suitable residences in "a noble and joyous city, unbelievably white." Questionless, the apostrophe, no less than the prediction, is "pleasant" to the apostrophized, his chosen and enormous audience; and as such is well received by the majority, who according to our theories of government are always right. Yet to some carping few of us (who read the daily papers, say) this sentiment now seems peculiarly anachronistic and irrational. The world to us is not very strikingly suggestive of a cosmic gumdrop variegated by oceans of molasses: we dispute if Omnipotence was ever, at any time, a confectioner's apprentice: and to us whatever workmen may have been employed in laying out that "noble and joyous city" appear undoubtedly to have gone on strike. So we remember Mr. Tarkington's own story of Lukens and the advice therein, when dealing with a popular novelist, to "treat him with silent contempt or a brick." And we reflect that Mr. Tarkington is certainly not a person to be treated with silent contempt. . .

For Mr. Tarkington has not mere talent but an uncontrollable wizardry that defies concealment, even by the livery of a popular novelist. The winding-up of the William Sylvanus Baxter stories, for example, is just the species of necromancy attainable by no other living author; so that a theatre wherein but now the humor of sitting upon wet paint and the mirthful aspect of a person vomiting have made

304

their bids for popular applause, is shaken to
its low foundation by the departing rumble of
a "pompous train," and unsuspected casements
open upon Fairy Land. Nor is the ending of
The Turmoil, technically, a whit inferior.
Here, though, with due respect to the recorded
verdict of Mr. W. D. Howells, one does not
"stand on tiptoe" to reach an effect so beautiful and unpredictable and so eminently "as
it ought to be." Instead, one is rather inclined
to kneel.

For here—and in how many other places!—
Mr. Tarkington displays a form of wealth which
should not be exempt from fair taxation. . .
And in fine, it all comes back to this: to write
"best sellers" is by ordinary a harmless and
very often a philanthropic performance; but in
Mr. Tarkington's case it is a misappropriation
of funds.

You perceive that Coleridge was perfectly
right—"and to be wroth with one we love doth
work like madness in the brain." Mr. Tarkington is a gentleman whose ability none of us
has any choice save cordially to love, and to
revere. It is for that reason I resent its waste,
and voice my resentment unwillingly. In short,
I throw my brick with one hand, and with the

other remove my hat. And to many this well
may seem the inkiest ingratitude, for one half-
moment to begrudge prosperity and wide applause to a person who has purveyed so many
enjoyable half-hours. But in cold earnest one
of the most dire calamities that ever befell
American literature was the commercial success
of *The Gentleman from Indiana,* so closely followed by the popular triumph of *Monsieur
Beaucaire.* For this double misfortune has
since bred such concessions by Mr. Tarkington,
to the necessity of being "pleasant," as would
seem amply to justify a remission of that
necessity, at all events among the admirers of
his ability as distinguished from its employment. And the pathos of it all is but augmented
by the circumstance that both of these novels
were quite fine enough to have "fallen flat,"
and so have left Mr. Tarkington to write in
rational obscurity a book commensurate with
his intelligence.

"Is that time dead?—lo, with a little Penrod
he has but touched the honey of romance" since
then, and thus has very, very slightly dissipated
its saccharinity. Still, we who have read all his
stories with resentful admiration cannot but
hopefully consider the date of Mr. Tarkington's

birth, and reflect that the really incurable optimism of senility remains a comfortably remote affair. Religion too assures us that there is always hope for a change of heart, if not for any actual regaining of the Biblical view—which, to be sure, is peculiarly ophthalmic as to the far-and-wide existence of "good and dear and beautiful people" and is unlikely ever to be taken seriously by Americans. No less, the fact remains that out of forty-nine years of living Mr. Tarkington has thus far given us only *Seventeen*. Nor would this matter were Mr. Tarkington a Barclay or a Harrison, or even the mental and artistic equal of the trio's far more popular rival, Mr. Harold Bell Wright. But Mr. Tarkington had genius. That is even more tragic than the "pleasant" ending of *The Magnificent Ambersons*. . .

9

Thus we approach the master of them all. And it is not without—upon the whole—exhilarating significance that by long odds the most popular author typewriting to-day is Mr. Harold Bell Wright. . . For in this matter of killing time he stands pre-eminent, like a David among these chirographic Sauls, and to their thousands he has slain his ten thousands of unoccupied half-hours.

This worthy representative of our popular standards in reading-matter during the opening years of the twentieth century, has been the target of so much more or less envious ridicule that to me it has proved almost a pleasure to read enough whole pages in his books to discover that there is absolutely nothing laughable about Mr. Wright. To the contrary, his novels are masterpieces in the always popular *genre ennuyeux*. A fly-leaf to the van of one of them asserts that the source of its author's power "is the same God-given secret that inspired Shakespeare and upheld Dickens." But it is hardly describable as a secret that dullness is the hall-mark of efficient people, in writing as elsewhere: and however liberal the endowments which enabled Dickens to write *Little Dorrit*, and Shakespeare to make an unfavorable impression on Mr. Shaw, one may reasonably question if, after all, these writers are the happiest analogues. Indeed, whatever their eminence in other respects, Mr. Wright is beyond comparison their superior in that especial sort of tediousness which, above all other natural gifts, Americans instinctively revere and trust.

308

. . Should proof be seriously demanded **that** as a nation we distrust brilliancy, it is **always** possible to produce the unanswerable list **of our** Presidents, and the *Congressional Record* **also** might be consulted for valuable **documentary** evidence. All democratic government, **though,** is of course based on the axiom that the **man** of average intelligence is in theory equal **to a** person of exceptional endowments, and in **prac-** tise the superior by reason of numbers: **and** that the average man is dull nobody can **well** dispute without furnishing a striking **example** to offset his contention. . . And for the **rest,** there is past doubt a tendency, among the **very** dull, to decry dullness, much as **millionaires** are prone to assure you that money does **not** always make for happiness: but to the **consid-** erate person a sufficient amount of **obtuseness** shows alike as the best possible armor in **life's** warfare at large, and the most **companionable** of traits in the home-circle, where it **unfailingly** flatters one's sense of superiority.

Now Mr. Harold Bell Wright has that **unerr-** ing accuracy in catering to the **commonplace** which first made *vers libre* readable, in **the** poems of Martin Farquahar Tupper. Nor is **it** possible for the most atrabilious contemner **of** popular taste to contend that Mr. Wright's books are badly written, for this author's avoidance of thought is made clear in perfectly presentable English, and in at least the style of its expression compares very creditably with the average Pastoral Letter.

Through five hundred generous pages his stories move with never an incongruous taint of liveliness or wit or imagination, narrating how the heroine decorously acquired an impeccable male admirer, and how the two of them, after a sufficing number of other calamities, were eventually married to each other. Money, of course, has come to them in consonance with the financial system of authentic noveldom, whereby material success is nicely graduated to everybody's domestic virtues. Yet in the mean time all well-to-do persons have proved so uniformly dishonest and contemptible and dissolute that it is not without misgivings one leaves the meritorious couple established in what has been aforetime described as the lap of luxury: and meanwhile God has been the subject of a great many complimentary remarks. For Mr. Wright's is precisely that conservative and unblushingly platitudinous dullness, of which every syllable reeks with 'wholesome sentiment,'' such as we take comfort to see represented in our senate-chambers, and to nod under on Sabbath mornings, and to retail to our helpless children. There is no walk in life in which this especial form of hebetude is not assured of meeting with respectful attention: and its claim to be esteemed a literary merit is, at the very worst, quite as well-founded as its age-old privilege to grace the rostrum and adorn the vestry.

It may well be the multitudinous readers of Mr. Wright who are our true art critics. They independently appraise that which they read. For they alone without any amazement recognize that the purpose of art is, not at all to record adroitly some personal or purloined idea in paint or clay or carbon-copies, but to evoke his idea in the brain-cells of other people; and that when art does not do this the artist has failed. . . It is not unsalutary to test one of them, with Walter Pater, say,—''To burn always with this gem-like flame, to maintain this ecstasy, is success in life,'' and so on. To the general reader the first clause suggests, if anything, Gehenna, and the second, habitual intoxication; neither of which impresses him as a likely avenue to the bank-account and lim-

ousine that brevet success in life: and more
over, he will point out with perfect justice that
flames, whatever else they may be, are not
"gem-like." It matters little whether there
after, in his figurative vernacular, he decrees
this "high-brow stuff" to be over his head or
beneath consideration: by either trope he voices
the fact that it has missed him, and the ques
tion, after all, is one of markmanship.

Here Pater's artifice, in short, has failed to
create art: for the idea has not been trans
ferred. The artifice of Mr. Harold Bell
Wright, however, such as it is, has sped true
as an arrow to the reader's prejudices. The
story, unquestionably, is rather stupid, with
something of the staleness of last week's news
paper: but imperfect human nature humbly
recognizes, in the light of experience, that it is
always bored by sustaining improvement.
Moreover, you must remember that, as sug
gested elsewhere, the general reader does not
turn to fiction with any expectation of positive
pleasure, but with the less ambitious aspiration
of killing time: he takes up a book when there
is nothing else conceivable to do, and then only.
For the rest, it is generally conceded that all
rich people lead deplorable private lives, of

which the more said the better as touches the
interest of that supplement to the Sunday paper
wherein the fashionable scandals of the reading-matter appropriately consort with the calumnies of the photographer. Then, too, that
high-minded artizans possessing fine heads of
hair invariably fade from observation in the
embrace of opulence and feminine arms, is a
well-known phenomenon susceptible of instant
proof through a visit to the nearest cinematograph. And finally, the man and the girl vie
with each other in discoursing "wholesome sentiment," and are such sweet and noble characters as the reader always knew existed somewhere, and is going to emulate to-morrow or, at
any rate, next month: for he, too, can procras-
tinate as amiably as far more cultured persons.
And he, too, has his dim notion of men "as they
ought to be." . .

The general reader, in a word, is punctiliously following Pater's exhortation, however
unintentionally; and is deriving that noble
pleasure which comes from exercising the highest reach of your endowments. It is the pleasure one man derives from writing the Second
Part of *Faust,* and another from playing chess,
—the pleasure of using the finest part of your

mind, such as it is, to its fullest extent, whatever that may happen to be. Where Mr. Wright can rouse this pleasure it is thus with perfect justice that Mr. Wright is greeted as a serious and successful artist. And this truth is in no way affected by the limited number of endowments possessed, and therefore brought to exercise, by the general reader: as I just pointed out in speaking of *Queed*, a mediocre book alone can bring out that which is best in a mediocre person: and a race-horse may very conscientiously enjoy and take credit for his work without qualms over his failure to have been born a centipede.

So when all is done, "Now, that's what I call a pretty good story," says the general reader, intrepidly appraising his own reading-matter. He thereby proves as indisputably that Mr. Wright is really an artist as that he himself is a competent art-critic. . . For in most cases, this unarrogant verdict records the fact that yet another book has momentarily evoked belief that—by and large—the Recording Angel is writing a pretty good story. A rather tawdry book has roused the speaker (as no amount of judicious writing could ever hope to do) from that workaday existence which is common to

314

mankind,—made up of tedious unimportant tasks and useless little habits,—to proud assurance that life is not a blind and aimless business, not all a hopeless waste and confusion: and that he himself, however gross and weak an animal in the revelation of his past antics, will presently be strong and excellent and wise, and his existence a pageant. And to create this assurance is the purpose of all art. . . And in life, of course, the demiurgic spirit of romance induces this dynamic illusion in every moment of life, since without it men to-day would not consent to live. I need hardly say that in promoting any and all illusions romance has no more potent ally, anywhere, than dullness. . .

10

So we attain the reassuring conclusion that the arbiters, both as to the popular appeal and as to the ultimate survival of any book, are our general human inadequacy and our general human resolution never to acknowledge this inadequacy. For our dullness and our vanity— as you perceive, I trust, by this?—are the dependable arbiters of every affair in human life. And luckily for us, they bid fair, too, to be the arbiters of life's final outcome.

Through a merciful dispensation, we are one and all of us created very vain and very dull: and by utilizing these invaluable qualities the demiurgic spirit of romance will yet contrive a world "as it ought to be." Vanity it is that pricks us indefatigably to play the ape to every dream romance induces; yet vanity is but the stirrup-cup: and urgent need arises that human dullness retain us (as it does) securely blinded, lest we observe the wayside horrors of our journey and go mad. One moment of clear vision as to man's plight in the universe would be quite sufficient to set the most philosophic gibbering. Meanwhile with bandaged eyes we advance: and human sanity is guarded by the brave and pitiable and tireless dullness of mankind. . . Yet note how varied are the amiable activities of human dullness, which tend alike to protect and to enliven human progress! Dullness it is, of course, that brews and quaffs Dutch courage in the form of popular novels, and hoards its "literary classics," as sentimental persons treasure old letters (because this faded writing once was necromancy), in a very rarely visited attic. . . But dullness, too, it is that fosters salutary optimism as to the destiny of mankind, in flat defiance of every-

316

thing mankind can do, and does unblushingly. And dullness likewise nurtures all our general faith in the peculiar sanctity of anything which one has seen done often enough, and our reverence for whatever is sufficiently hackneyed; since dullness, naturally, ascribes no slight importance to itself. . . Then, too, how magnanimously does dullness, in you and me and our moonstruck compeers, dispose of its one fervent scudding moment of ability to do anything at all, by devoting it to the creation of "art"; so that some erroneous impression, based upon the talebearing of five perfidious senses (and painfully worked out to a *non sequitur,* by the rattletrap mechanism of an "artist's" lop-sided brain), may be preserved for posterity's misguidance and well-being. In graver circles, dullness—sometimes mitred, sometimes eruptive with forensic platitudes, and at its most terrible with a black cap adorning its inertia,—invents and codifies religion, and makes euphonious noises about "right" and "wrong," as an ornate and stately method of imposing the local by-laws. Equally among those favored mortals whom the income tax annoys does a kindred form of dullness become axiomatic about common-sense and "being practical," as

the impedimenta peculiarly requisite to wing-
less bipeds when left to their own devices
among much non-committal stardrift. . . Dullness it is that, signally, esteems itself well
worthy of perpetuation; and in the action seeks
to love, in the quite staggering faith that presently by some human being of the opposite sex
love will be merited. And finally dullness it is
that lifts up heart and voice alike, to view a
parasite infesting the epidermis of a midge
among the planets, and cries, *Behold, this is the
child of God All-mighty and All-worshipful,
made in the likeness of his Father!* . . These
and how many other wholesome miracles are
daily brought about by our dullness, by our
brave and pitiable and tireless dullness, by our
really majestic dullness, in firm alliance with
the demiurgic spirit of romance. . . But upon
these amiable activities I shall dilate no further,
lest you declare my encomiums somewhat less
adequately to praise the dullness of mankind
than to illustrate it: yet you perceive, I trust,
that our dullness is our one quite priceless possession.

And so it is dullness alone which enables us
to hurl defiance at "realism": for these illusions that are born of romance, and are nursed

by dullness, serve as our curveting and prancing escort, and keep at bay all interference, as we pass in a straggling caravan, with death already hot upon the trail, and human nature clogging every step like gyves. And thus protected, to-day as always, our caravan accepts romance for guide; and strains and flounders toward goals which stay remote, and yet are fairly discernible. For that to which romance conducts, in all the affairs of life (concluded John Charteris), is plain enough,—distinction and clarity, and beauty and symmetry, and tenderness and truth and urbanity.

X
WHEREIN WE AWAIT

—There was a deal said, sir—what with one thing leading to another, as it were—but no great harm done after all.

—And no good either, you may depend upon it, Dabney. . . . There is never any good comes of interminable palavering. . . This is a case that calls for action, and for instant action, by George!

—Just as you say, sir, no doubt And yet—well, in a manner of speaking, sir, and considering everything—why, what on earth is anybody able to do?

—I am sure I don't know. But that does not in the least alter the principle of the thing.

—*In Old Lichfield*

X

Wherein We Await

HERE for a moment John Charteris ceased talking. He, at least, seemed not fatigued: but the venerable tall clock behind him again had asthmatically cleared its throat; and now, in thin unresonant tones, which suggested the beating of a pencil on the bottom of a tin pan, was striking five: so Charteris had paused, provisionally. And I seized the chance.

Said I:

—So here we are back again precisely where we started, with a strained pose upon the same half-truth. Now, Charteris, suppose you let me talk a little!

His hands went out in a wide gesture of magnanimity. . .

I continued:

—Where is one to begin, though! . . Well, I shall generously say at outset that not in a long time have I heard a discourse so insincere. It is an apology for romance by a man who believes that romance is dead beyond resurrection; and who considers therefore that to romance may be attributed every imaginable virtue, without any imaginable consequences. It is a tissue of wild errors, deceitfully glossed with the unreasonableness of a person who is really in earnest; so that, I confess, I was at first quite taken in, and fancied you to be lamenting with honest grief the world's lost youth.

Said Charteris:

—Ah, but who can with honesty lament the passing of youth? No, youth remains current everywhere, though, like all other forms of currency, its only value is that it purchases something else. For the rest, far from deploring that our present-day reading-matter is no longer youthful, I have just voiced unfeigned regret that it is childish.

—But, my dear Charteris, consider soberly this conceit of yours! Of course, I must protest that you have been shamefully unfair with "realism" throughout: for however pleasingly you have defined romance—by implication, at least—you have left "realism" indeterminate after so many hours of abusing it.

Charteris shrugged: but he said nothing.

324

And I continued my effort to bring him to reason:

—Indeed, your major and minor premises seem to run thus: romance in literature is that method, governed by that viewpoint, in which resides all virtue; and "realism" is precisely the reverse. To your hearer you leave the completion of this imperfect syllogism. Now that is an excellent way to convince the unwary: it is, on the other hand, a poor method of discovering truth.

John Charteris said:

—If I indeed left "realism" indeterminate, it was merely because I hesitated to define the unmentionable. "Realism"—not only in writing, but in every one of its evincements—is the fallacy that our mile-posts are as worthy of consideration as our goal; and that the especial post we are now passing reveals an eternal verity. As a matter of fact, mile-posts by ordinary reveal the pretensions of a tradesman who believes in advertising,—which very possibly accounts for the manner of our more generally esteemed "realists," in every field of human action. So "realism" too becomes an art of sorts, a minor art like music or hair-dressing.

325

"Realism" is the art of being superficial seriously.

2

—Permit me, Charteris, none the less, to restate your principal thesis as it concerns the writer's craft—

Now, curiously enough, the little novelist appeared vexed.

—My dear fellow, my very dear fellow (John Charteris inquired, with careful and laborious patience), but have I really seemed to you tonight to be talking about books and how books should be written? For in that event, I have failed very disastrously. My target was not at all "literary." Instead, I have attempted to expound man's proper attitude toward the universe he temporarily infests; and to show you that this must always be a purely romantic attitude which is in no wise concerned with facts. Yes, I can but repeat my golden rule for æsthetic conduct: there should be no trifling with facts.

—But, Charteris, from the very beginning you have been talking about books and the makers of books—

John Charteris shook his head. He declared:

—It is discouraging: but the wounds of a friend are proverbially faithful. I have talked for a not inconsiderable while, with perfect honesty and the best of my ability: and the upshot is that my audience evinces no least shadowy comprehension of what I have been talking about. The writer's craft, quotha!

But without heeding the grimaces of Charteris, I went on rationally:

—Romance, I infer, is the expression of an attitude which views life with profound distrust, as a business of exceeding dullness and of very little worth; and which therefore seeks for beauty by an abandonment of the facts of living. Living is a drab transaction, a concatenation of unimportant events: man is impotent and aimless: beauty, and indeed all the fine things which you desiderate in literature—and in your personal existence, I suspect—are nowhere attainable save in imagination. To the problem of living, romance propounds the only possible answer, which is, not understanding, but escape. And the method of that escape is, you imply, the creation of a pleasing dream, which will somehow engender a reality as lovely. So romance in literature invents its "dynamic illusions"—Ibsen called them vital

327

lies, did he not?—to the sole end that mankind may play Peter Ibbetson upon a cosmic scale. This I take to be the doctrine of your Economists.

—Oh, but continue, pray! said Charteris. Continue, since you are bent upon reducing all my wasted eloquence to a lecture on novel-writing!

—Well, I shall avoid the obvious comment that your viewpoint outdoes in pessimism the ugliest vision of the "realist"; and that it has its root in cowardice; and, finally, that it presents the difficulty which Mr. Gilbert Chesterton once voiced,—That what is wrong with the world is that no man can say what would be right with it. This applies to Sophocles as poignantly as to John Charteris. Nor will I insist that very often what you have regarded as beautiful I with equal conviction have deemed merely pretty.

—I am confuted, John Charteris replied, in that any unmade comment is unanswerable. . . Otherwise, I would agree that quite obviously the world is made uninhabitable by the density of its inhabitants. I might even, very rudely, cite contiguous evidence. . . As for cowardice, I might point out that clear thinking is everywhere indoctrinated by that instructor who alone can teach the tortoise to run, and the cornered rat to fight, and human beings to be rational. And had you vocally denied my doctrines on the ground of their ugliness, I would have flung full in your face earthquakes and cloudbursts and hyenas and rhinoceroses and diseases and germs and intellectual women; and the unlovable senility of aged persons, which converts the very tenderest affection into resigned endurance of its object as an unavoidable nuisance; and the cruel and filthy process of birth; and the unspeakable corruption of death: and I would have given you untrammeled leave to deduce from the ugliness of these things that they are all untrue. . . But since you graciously keep silence, so must I.

3

—All that, my friend, is equivocation pure and simple. However, let me defer your quibble for a moment, Charteris. For I want to point out with emphatic seriousness one quality which you have overlooked in cataloging the desirable ingredients of literature—

—But literature is really not, I must submit with Gautier, a sort of soup stock, which one may flavor to every individual taste by putting this and that into the pot.

—You have said, then, Charteris, that these are the auctorial virtues *par excellence:* distinction and clarity, beauty and symmetry, and tenderness and truth and urbanity. These are good, I grant: and it may be upon a mere matter of words that we differ. Yet it seems to me that all books have been made re-readable through the possession, not of these qualities alone, but of one other which is salt to them all—and that quality is gusto.

—You employ an excellent sonorous word, conceded Charteris. And perhaps to you this use of it may even seem to have some meaning?

—Why, to me it appears that all enduring books, of however delicate a texture, have possessed a—well, we will say, a heartiness akin to the smacking of lips over a good dish. It is not joy, for many joyless writers have displayed it; and it is often inherent in the blackest of tragedies. It is not ecstasy, although to ecstasy it may approach. I think it is almost a physical thing: it certainly involves a complete surrender to life, and an absorption of one's self in the functions of being. It is a drunkenness of the soul, perhaps: it is allied to that fierce pain and joy which we call ecstatic living, and which the creative artist must always seek to reproduce in his work, just as does every adequately existing person still reproduce it now and then in corporal life—and whether through gross sins or high-flown abnegations is, to the artist at least, quite immaterial. Yes, gusto, I would say, is the very life-blood of art: and solely by the measure of art's possession of what I have called gusto does art overtop life, when art is able to distill the quintessence of that which in reality is always more or less transitory and alloyed.

John Charteris said:

—Undoubtedly I failed to stipulate that the creative artist should write with what you describe as "gusto": indeed, I would as soon have thought of suggesting that he write with his hand. For the sole point upon which fine literature and reading-matter and all the uncontested axioms of mankind are quite at one, is in assuming mankind to be superhuman. Through this protective instinct the artist will as an affair of course, in his depiction of human beings, exaggerate everything. All passions, naturally, will be studied by him, as with a microscope, whereunder men's emotions will figure as untamed leviathans that ramp quite awe-inspiringly.

Now Charteris was so outrageously perverting my meaning that I would have interrupted him. But he continued:

—No, you and I can differ but upon the question as to whether in corporal life some "adequately existing person" does now and then reproduce anything of this sort. With the wide-spread tradition that he does we ought to deal as open-mindedly as with the equally well-known myth of George and the Dragon or of the Cat and the Fiddle. No doubt, one might infer, once more upon advisement of the morning-paper, that no longer ago than yesterday a respectable number of not at all respectable people were brought through the indulgence of some such "gusto" into publicity and police-stations: but, even in pursuit of a really "adequate" scheme of living, one hesitates to accept these folk as patterns: and the wiser of us will not quite thus tumultuously rush into the dock. For to comparatively intelligent persons self-control is a more common and less difficult virtue than any intelligent person would dream of admitting. Passion does not rouse the vast majority of us to any outbreak, or even to eloquence: perhaps, indeed, nothing can ever do that save dread of public opinion. In purely personal matters the disheartening fact is that we encounter crises with commonplaces, and the important scenes of one's life are rendered inefficiently, at their only performance. How can this be otherwise, when all the while we are vexatiously aware that our emotions are unfit to the occasion? For it is the actual reflection of every considerate person at the climax of some great joy or crime or grief, that his emotion is neither so fine nor so absorbing as he had anticipated. It follows, of course, that everyone of us is forever after resolute to conceal this failure, especially from himself. . . So it is not quite for the reason which you advance that I accept your dictum as to art's overtopping life through art's ability to distill the quintessence of that which, in ephemeral reality, is transitory and alloyed. Still, I accept it.

4

—My dear Charteris, I really must in passing congratulate you upon your retention of youth. I had thought it the peculiar privilege of immaturity to view mankind and God with doleful eyes. But here am I, quick with the wisdom of my generation, compelled to shout denial of your doctrines from comparatively roseate heights, for all that you are by some twenty-two years my senior, and your opinions ought in consequence to be already gilded by a setting sun. Instead, you appraise earth in the dumps. . . Well, I let pass that pose, out of commingled respect for its antiquity and youthfulness. Meanwhile, I do agree with you when you say all enduring literature in the past has been of the romantic quality you describe, from whatever various standpoints this quality has been apprehended. And it is true that surface faithfulness alone, such as many modern novelists seek to achieve, is the emptiest of artistic aims. I even grant you it is better to lie pleasingly. . . Indeed, despite your wilful blindness as to the true value of "realism," your slurs upon the practised methods of producing "realistic" art compose a valuable recipe. It is merely because I think you have ignored some essentials that I venture, upon this subject also, to be banal. Bear with me, then, while I recite a modest credo of my own. . . I too believe it is more important that literature should be true to life than that it should inventory life's mannerisms. I believe we can never be concerned by any man or woman in a book if we do not—at least while the book's spell is on us—put very cordial faith in that person's existence, and share in the emotional atmosphere of the scene. But I likewise believe that the illusion of reality can be produced by the romantic or the "realistic" method, either one, or even by the two commingled, provided always that the artist, given insight, is sincerely striving to show fundamental things as he sees them, and thereby, perhaps, to hint at their true and unknowable nature.

—Ah, but (said Charteris) I have freely conceded that this illusion can be produced in many cases even by the Wright method. It is merely a question of how much intelligence the reader lacks. For the rest, your "if" has somewhat the impressive vacuity of an address to Congress. Were I inclined to daring metaphor, I would suggest that your cloudy "if" ambiguously wreathes the black hole of "realism" with such vaporings as ordinarily emanate from a white house.

—Well! then I mouth my platitudes in very respectable company. Whereas you—but just consider whither you would lead us with your Economist doctrines—say, with your doctrine of original dullness! Grant that man is as inadequate as you please, and living as uneventful: no less, the jogtrot way is sometimes illumined and is made august by flashes struck from midnights (to pervert Browning to my own uses), and still even the most humble of us have our exalted moments. And these moments, I contend, it is the business of the artist, romanticist and "realist" alike, to interpret for us and, if he can, to evaluate them in terms of approximate eternity.

—It is just possible, John Charteris suggested, that the poor dear man may fall a shade short of omniscience. I at least have encountered writers with this defect, although none, of course, who was conscious of it. . . And I forbear to inquire as to the no doubt interesting process of evaluating anything in "terms of approximate eternity," simply because this also sounds delightfully presidential, and suggests the swish of Mrs. Partington's not uncelebrated broom. On second thought, though, I retract the "presidential": your words are such stuff as deans are made on.

5

To Charteris I nodded now in cordial assent. Said I:

—Perverted proverbs are a little old-fashioned, aren't they, nowadays? Still, I hail gladly both your fleering analogues. For art is truly "a branch of pedagogy," because the artist is affiliated to priesthood. To only a few of us is it given, or desirable, to see within. The majority must for practical purposes dissever dreams from the business of existence: dreams are not our *métier*, and that is all there is to it. Yet since it is our nature to learn by parables, we turn to the artist who is also a seer, in search of entertainment, and more or less consciously hoping to acquire understanding. . . What does it matter, then, the seer's "method"? You should remember Chantecler's experience with "methods." No, whether the seer's text be some impartially considered facts about John Jones, or whether he clothe his puppets with such a bright and exquisite tissue of prevarication as enmeshes the personality of King Arthur or Jeanne Darc or Lee or Lincoln, or any other high-minded figment of patriotic self-complacency—this "method," I repeat, must always stay a circumstance of conspicuous unimportance. We merely ask that our story treat of such a man as captures our attention; and that through the lights and shadows of his fortunes may glimmer something like an answer to the great question which I can only word as "What is it all up to?" Yes, that is really the one thing we need to know about the universe, nowadays: and our need is heavy and quenchless. . . You see, my creed says nothing about "style," and makes no caustic remarks as to the taste of my fellow citizens. But you are none the less aware of how firm my faith is in the axiom that the best of "styles" is the simplest and the least affected: and I believe that saying applies with equal truth to the best of our fellow citizens. For the rest, I would merely express the "reaction" to that portion of your talk which touches on the writer's craft, by one who—let us say—is instantly aware of his preference for Thackeray whenever anybody mentions Dickens; and who comprehends without bitterness that it is the business of the author, and not of the public, to see that the distinction between literature and reading-matter be rendered less invidious, by proving that literature may be both. For I know that what is one man's inspiration is another's soporific; and that to the fellow craftsman only is the craftsman's skill apparent; and that, no less, when one person anywhere has

voiced a tonic truth or some great-hearted lie
(for these are really truths in embryo), that
utterance must quite inevitably become what
is both less and more than literature: for it
will be in time a commonplace of daily speech
among the simplest and the least affected people; and so will live when countless masterpieces and their makers are forgotten.

6

Again John Charteris grimaced. He spread
those eloquent soft hands of his, palms upward.
He said:

—Thus you affirm that art is an important form of religion; while I have pointed out
that religion is one of the loveliest forms of
art. Our final difference is, let us say, but one
of terms—which are quite possibly "of approximate eternity." So let us leave them, then,
agreeing simply that art and religion are kindred. . . And truly as to the origin of either
what man can utter anything save his guesses?
None now remembers who first thought of any
god: all the creators of religion are become un-
honored dust; and it is only the anthologists,
such as Buddha and Mohammed and Zoroaster
and Christ and Moses and Confucius, who have

bequeathed imperishable names to serve as weapons for the weak, as well as for the fool and the fanatic. So it has always been in every field of artistic creation. Indeed, a very cogent proof that art is akin to religion lies in the fact that, will you or nill you, you contribute to the welfare of some form of each. In each the only feasible way to attack a tenet is to found a schism: so that even atheists and the contributors to magazines must perforce adhere to their common creed, of denying plausibility to personal creation. . . Moreover, religion and art alone take tender care of their unprofitable servants. Thus for the clergy who find Christian tenets impracticable there are always bishoprics: whereas it is the sure reward of every unsuccessful artist that he shall be forgotten, and so shall be no longer inadequate. Say that his vision founders in the form of a book! Well, the man passes; and the milk of human kindness obliterates the ink he spattered. But a few of his words, and of the words of many other men who failed as literary artists, will be repeated and re-echoed, in idle hearthside talk, because there is something in them, though not very much: and presently time will bring forth the brain to fuse, and the tongue to utter, all these old disregarded little sayings in harmony. And then these men will have become a legendary whole: and each life's work will live, despite its failure, and will survive if but as a half-sentence or as some happy phrase. That outcome certainly is not prodigious. But then these fragments will live on eternally; and Shakespeare's lordliest fancy can hardly hope to do much more. These fragments will not be pondered over; and they will never wring tears and themes from schoolboys: but they will be as threads in the stuff of which dreams are woven. In this much all shall serve the demiurgic spirit of romance: and even the feeble hand that failed, and the vain ambition which pitiably wrought its own burlesque, shall aid to shape dynamic illusions; and so in time will create reality.

—These, Charteris, are very certainly what Captain Fluellen was wont to commend for being "as prave words as you shall see in a summer's day." But I fancy they are not much more. And so, I give you over as incorrigible.

Now Charteris leaned back in his revolving chair, so that it creaked and tilted. His arms went up behind his head, in a long stretching gesture, and he yawned luxuriously. He said:

—But is not to be given over by one's friends the inevitable price of speaking the tongue of angels? I really wish you would not interrupt my periods. . . For, as I was going on to remark, by the elect anthologist will be pursued all the auctorial virtues: distinction and clarity, and beauty and symmetry, and tenderness and truth and urbanity. Thus it has been since the moon's nonage. And as I began by saying a few minutes ago, I believe that to-day, as always, it is only through the exercise of these virtues that any man may in reason attempt to insure his books against oblivion's voracity. . . But was it indeed a few moments ago that I began? . .

Charteris rose and pushed open one of the shutters. He stood thus, peering out into the green recesses of his garden, and blinking in a flood of clear gray light that showed him curiously sallow and withered and futile looking.

—Upon my word, said he, it is morning. I must have talked all night. And the dawn of this new day discovers me, after so many divigations, just where I started yesterday. Yes, it admits of any number of moral deductions. . .

For I have talked all night: and you have not even suspected what I was talking about.

342

I have spoken of the demiurgic spirit of romance, which by cajoling our inestimable vanity and dullness controls all human life, and profitably utilizes every blunder of human life; and I have spoken of existence from the one viewpoint which reveals in human life some possible significance: and all the while you believed that I was trying to voice my personal theory as to how novels ought to be written! Well, perhaps that is about as near as any one of us can ever come to understanding another: and even though the reflection has its dispiriting aspect, it strikingly exposes the futility of my talking further. That circumstance, at least, should be consolatory. . .

So I have wearied the night with much vain speech; and neither rhetoric nor candor has availed me anything. Yes, it admits of a vast number of moral deductions: but I prefer to regard myself symbolically, as an epitome of all mankind. For each of us is babbling in the night, and has no way to make his fellows understand just what he would be at. It may be there is some supernal audience which sees and hears with perfect comprehension? Yes, such of course may be the case. But in that event

343

I shudder to think of how we must provoke
and bore that audience. . .

7

Meanwhile (continued John Charteris) it is
strange to look out upon that quiet-colored
place of vacant lawns and undulating foliage,
where there appears to be no living thing anywhere save those querulous birds. Everywhere
it is a world of wavering verdancy, a twilit
world without any shadows or sharp fall of sun
rays, a world such as we attribute to the mer-
folk undersea—or, say, to the witch-woman's
occupancy. It is only my familiar garden, but
this trick of light estranges it. . . At dawn
you have the Chivalrous sense of being in a
place that is not home, and wherein something
is expected of you. Then, too, at dawn you
have a sense of imminent destiny, and feel that
what is going to happen to you is very generally
foreknown. Birds shrill of it, and it is about
this the trees hold conference, and the placid
sun seems to have risen to find how far the
matter has progressed. Eh, I am helpless in an
ambiguous place,—I and all my fellows, whom
I may not, quite, understand,—and there is no
escape from this unalterably ordered proces-

sion of sound and noise and color, save through death. And I do not know what death means, either. . . So I shall presently eat breakfast and enjoy it, and look over the morning-paper with interest, and then get to writing and find pleasure in that too,—I, who am under this inevitable sentence to a fate at which I cannot guess! It is in such a predicament that I find time to think seriously about literature, and to prattle about literature, and to ask this and that of literature, quite as if books or anything else could possibly matter, while that impends which is going to happen to me,—that unpredictable outcome of affairs which the dawn knows about. For very certainly at dawn there is abroad some force which foreknows all things. I sense its nearness and its contemplation of me, and I am frightened. . .

8

Meanwhile you voice a truth I had not hitherto perceived: I ask of literature precisely those things of which I feel the lack in my own life. I appeal for charity, and implore that literature afford me what I cannot come by in myself. . .

For I want distinction for that existence

which ought to be peculiarly mine, among my innumerable fellows who swarm about earth like ants. Yet which one of us is noticeably, or can be appreciably different, in this throng of human ephemeræ and all their millions and inestimable millions of millions of predecessors and oncoming progeny? And even though one mote may transiently appear exceptional, the distinction of those who in their heydays are "great" personages—much as the Emperor of Lilliput overtopped his subjects by the breadth of Captain Gulliver's nail,—must suffer loss with time, and must dwindle continuously, until at most the man's recorded name remains here and there in sundry pedants' libraries. There were how many dynasties of Pharaohs, each one of whom was absolute lord of the known world, and is to-day forgotten? Among the countless popes who one by one were adored as the regent of Heaven upon earth, how many persons can to-day distinguish? and does not time breed emperors and czars and presidents as plentiful as blackberries, and as little thought of when their season is out? For there is no perpetuity in human endeavor: we strut upon a quicksand: and all that any man may do for good or ill is presently forgotten, because it

346

does not matter. I wail to a familiar tune, of course, in this lament for the evanescence of human grandeur and the perishable renown of kings. And indeed to the statement that imperial Cæsar is turned to clay and Mizraim now cures wounds, and that in short Queen Anne is dead, we may agree lightly enough; for it is, after all, a matter of no personal concern: but how hard it is to concede that the banker and the rector and the traffic-officer, to whom we more immediately defer, and we ourselves, and the little gold heads of our children, may be of no importance, either! . . In art it may so happen that the thing which a man makes endures to be misunderstood and gabbled over: yet it is not the man himself. We retain the *Iliad,* but oblivion has swallowed Homer so deep that many question if he ever existed at all. . . So we pass as a cloud of gnats, where I want to live and be thought of, if only by myself, as a distinguishable entity. And such distinction is impossible in the long progress of suns, whereby in thought to separate the personality of any one man from all others that have lived, becomes a task to stagger Omniscience. . .

I want my life, the only life of which I am

assured, to have symmetry or, in default of that, at least to acquire some clarity. Surely it is not asking very much to wish that my personal conduct be intelligible to me! Yet it is forbidden to know for what purpose this universe was intended, to what end it was set a-going, or why I am here, or even what I had preferably do while here. It vaguely seems to me that I am expected to perform an allotted task, but as to what it is I have no notion. . . And indeed, what have I done hitherto, in the years behind me? There are some books to show as increment, as something which was not anywhere before I made it, and which even in bulk will replace my buried body, so that my life will be to mankind no loss materially. But the course of my life, when I look back, is as orderless as a trickle of water that is diverted and guided by every pebble and crevice and grass-root it encounters. I seem to have done nothing with pre-meditation, but rather, to have had things done to me. And for all the rest of my life, as I know now, I shall have to shave every morning in order to be ready for no more than this! . . I have attempted to make the best of my material circumstances always; nor do I see to-day how any widely varying course could have been wiser or even feasible: but material things have nothing to do with that life which moves in me. Why, then, should they direct and heighten and provoke and curb every action of life? It is against the tyranny of matter I would rebel,—against life's absolute need of food, and books, and fire, and clothing, and flesh, to touch and to inhabit, lest life perish. . . No, all that which I do here or refrain from doing lacks clarity, nor can I detect any symmetry anywhere, such as living would assuredly display, I think, if my progress were directed by any particular motive. . . It is all a muddling through, somehow, without any recognizable goal in view, and there is no explanation of the scuffle tendered or anywhere procurable. It merely seems that to go on living has become with me a habit. . .

And I want beauty in my life. I have seen beauty in a sunset and in the spring woods and in the eyes of divers women, but now these happy accidents of light and color no longer thrill me. And I want beauty in my life itself, rather than in such chances as befall it. It seems to me that many actions of my life were beautiful, very long ago, when I was young in an evanished world of friendly girls, who were all more lovely than any girl is nowadays. For women now are merely more or less good-looking, and as I know, their looks when at their best have been painstakingly enhanced and edited. . . But I would like this life which moves and yearns in me, to be able itself to attain to comeliness, though but in transitory performance. The life of a butterfly, for example, is just a graceful gesture: and yet, in that its loveliness is complete and perfectly rounded in itself, I envy this bright flicker through existence. And the nearest I can come to my ideal is punctiliously to pay my bills, be polite to my wife, and contribute to deserving charities: and the programme does not seem, somehow, quite adequate. There are my books, I know; and there is beauty "embalmed and treasured up" in many pages of my books, and in the books of other persons, too, which I may read at will: but this desire inborn in me is not to be satiated by making marks upon paper, nor by deciphering them. . . In short, I am enamored of that flawless beauty of which all poets have perturbedly divined the existence somewhere, and which life as men know it simply does not afford nor anywhere fore-see. . .

350

And tenderness, too—but does that appear a mawkish thing to desiderate in life? Well, to my finding human beings do not like one another. Indeed, why should they, being rational creatures? All babies have a temporary lien on tenderness, of course: and therefrom children too receive a dwindling income, although on looking back, you will recollect that your childhood was upon the whole a lonesome and much put-upon period. But all grown persons ineffably distrust one another. . . In courtship, I grant you, there is a passing aberration which often mimics tenderness, sometimes as the result of honest delusion, but more frequently as an ambuscade in the endless struggle between man and woman. Married people are not ever tender with each other, you will notice: if they are mutually civil it is much: and physical contacts apart, their relation is that of a very moderate intimacy. My own wife, at all events, I find an unfailing mystery, a Sphinx whose secrets I assume to be not worth knowing: and, as I am mildly thankful to narrate, she knows very little about me, and evinces as to my affairs no morbid interest. That is not to assert that if I were ill she would not nurse me through any imaginable contagion, nor that if she were drowning I would not plunge in after her, whatever my delinquencies at swimming: what I mean is that, pending such high crises, we tolerate each other amicably, and never think of doing more. . . And from our blood-kin we grow apart inevitably. Their lives and their interests are no longer the same as ours, and when we meet it is with conscious reservations and much manufactured talk. Besides, they know things about us which we resent. . . And with the rest of my fellows, I find that convention orders all our dealings, even with children, and we do and say what seems more or less expected. And I know that we distrust one another all the while, and instinctively conceal or misrepresent our actual thoughts and emotions when there is no very apparent need. . . Personally, I do not like human beings because I am not aware, upon the whole, of any generally distributed qualities which entitle them as a race to admiration and affection. But toward people in books—such as Mrs. Millamant, and Helen of Troy, and Bella Wilfer, and Mélusine, and Beatrix Esmond,—I may intelligently overflow with tenderness and caressing words, in part because they deserve it, and in part because I know they

352

will not suspect me of being "queer" or of having ulterior motives. . .

And I very often wish that I could know the truth about just any one circumstance connected with my life. . . Is the phantasmagoria of sound and noise and color really passing or is it all an illusion here in my brain? How do you know that you are not dreaming me, for instance? In your conceded dreams, I am sure, you must invent and see and listen to persons who for the while seem quite as real to you as I do now. As I do, you observe, I say! and what thing is it to which I so glibly refer as I? If you will try to form a notion of yourself, of the sort of a something that you suspect to inhabit and partially to control your flesh and blood body, you will encounter a walking bundle of superfluities: and when you mentally have put aside the extraneous things,—your garments and your members and your body, and your acquired habits and your appetites and your inherited traits and your prejudices, and all other appurtenances which considered separately you recognize to be no integral part of you,—there seems to remain in those pearl-colored brain-cells, wherein is your ultimate lair, very little save a faculty for receiving

353

sensations, of which you know the larger portion to be illusory. And surely, to be just a very gullible consciousness provisionally existing among inexplicable mysteries, is not an enviable plight. And yet this life—to which I cling tenaciously,—comes to no more. Meanwhile I hear men talk about "the truth"; and they even wager handsome sums upon their knowledge of it: but I align myself with "jesting Pilate," and echo the forlorn query that recorded time has left unanswered. . .

Then, last of all, I desiderate urbanity. I believe this is the rarest quality in the world. Indeed, it probably does not exist anywhere. A really urbane person—a mortal open-minded and affable to conviction of his own shortcomings and errors, and unguided in anything by irrational blind prejudices,—could not but in a world of men and women be regarded as a monster. We are all of us, as if by instinct, intolerant of that which is unfamiliar: we resent its impudence: and very much the same principle which prompts small boys to jeer at a straw-hat out of season induces their elders to send missionaries to the heathen. The history of the progress of the human race is but the picaresque romance of intolerance, a narrative of how—what is it Milton says?— "truth never came into the world but, like a bastard, to the ignominy of him that brought her forth, till time hath washed and salted the infant, declared her legitimate, and churched the father of his young Minerva." And I, who prattle to you, very candidly confess that I have no patience with other people's ideas unless they coincide with mine: for if the fellow be demonstrably wrong I am fretted by his stupidity, and if his notion seem more nearly right than mine I am infuriated. . . Yet I wish I could acquire urbanity, very much as I would like to have wings. For in default of it, I cannot even manage to be civil to that piteous thing called human nature, or to view its parasites, whether they be politicians or clergymen or popular authors, with one half the commiseration which the shifts they are put to, quite certainly, would rouse in the urbane. . .

9

So I in point of fact desire of literature, just as you guessed, precisely those things of which I most poignantly and most constantly feel the lack in my own life. And it is that which romance affords her postulants. The philtres of romance are brewed to free us from this unsatisfying life that is calendared by fiscal years, and to contrive a less disastrous elusion of our own personalities than many seek dispersedly in drink and drugs and lust and fanaticism, and sometimes in death. For, beset by his own rationality, the normal man is goaded to evade the strictures of his normal life, upon the incontestable ground that it is a stupid and unlovely routine; and to escape likewise from his own personality, which bores him quite as much as it does his associates. So he hurtles into these very various roads from reality, precisely as a goaded sheep flees without notice of what lies ahead. . .

And romance tricks him, but not to his harm. For, be it remembered that man alone of animals plays the ape to his dreams. Romance it is undoubtedly who whispers to every man that life is not a blind and aimless business, not all a hopeless waste and confusion; and that his existence is a pageant (appreciatively observed by divine spectators), and that he is strong and excellent and wise: and to romance he listens, willing and thrice willing to be cheated by the honeyed fiction. The things of which romance assures him are very far from true: yet it is solely by believing himself a creature but little lower than the cherubim that man has by interminable small degrees become, upon the whole, distinctly superior to the chimpanzee: so that, however extravagant may seem these flattering whispers to-day, they were immeasureably more remote from veracity when men first began to listen to their sugared susurrus, and steadily the discrepancy lessens. To-day these things seem quite as preposterous to calm consideration as did flying yesterday: and so, to the Gradgrindians, romance appears to discourse foolishly, and incurs the common fate of prophets: for it is about to-morrow and about the day after to-morrow, that romance is talking, by means of parables. And all the while man plays the ape to fairer and yet fairer dreams, and practise strengthens him at mimickry. . .

10

To what does the whole business tend?—why, how in heaven's name should I know? We can but be content to note that all goes forward, toward something. . . It may be that we are nocturnal creatures perturbed by rumors of a dawn which comes inevitably, as prologue to a day wherein we and our children have no part whatever. It may be that when our arboreal propositus descended from his palm-tree and began to walk upright about the earth, his progeny were forthwith committed to a journey in which to-day is only a way-station. Yet I prefer to take it that we are components of an unfinished world, and that we are but as seething atoms which ferment toward its making, if merely because man as he now exists can hardly be the finished product of any Creator whom one could very heartily revere. We are being made into something quite unpredictable, I imagine: and through the purging and the smelting, we are sustained by an instinctive knowledge that we are being made into something better. For this we know, quite incommunicably, and yet as surely as we know that we will to have it thus.

And it is this will that stirs in us to have the creatures of earth and the affairs of earth, not as they are, but "as they ought to be," which we call romance. But when we note how visibly it sways all life we perceive that we are talking about God.

EXPLICIT ULTRA VITAM

SOME OTHER BOOKS BY MR. CABELL

(With Tributes of the Press)

Mr. Cabell's style of writing bristles with the maudlin and lachrymose romantics such as fascinate the shop-girls in the pages of George Barr McCutcheon. And then too has Mr. Cabell's irony a way of losing itself in the burbles of profound and academic inanities. Also he is lacking in the courage of his disillusion, and . . . because of this lack of courage does his irony become a sort of meandering wistfulness like the whine of a little old man suffering from false teeth. Finally Mr. Cabell is lacking as a poet. He is unable to create those illusions so necessary for the reality of fiction. . . . So Cabell remains the sardonic professor mouthing in the boring rhetoric of the classroom.—BEN HECHT, in *The Chicago News*.

THE CREAM OF THE JEST

(A Comedy of Evasions)

Mr. Cabell is a self-conscious sentimentalist, hopelessly so. In this book he goes further in speculative and vague imaginings than he has ever ventured before, with the result that he has developed to an amazing extent a purposeless fantasy. Mr. Cabell is guilty also of a curious intellectual egotism. He thus assumes on the part of the reader a necessary interest and sympathy, perhaps even admiration, that are hardly justified by the book itself. The result is a mystery without interest, a fanciful construction of character and experience that does not stir the fancy.—*New Orleans Picayune.*

The author fails of making his dull characters humanely pitiable. But it is material for a short story, not for a novel. A single slight situation, and a group of persons who do not act as or change from the first page to the last are not heavy enough to weight a volume.—*New York Post.*

A rambling story, without form, and told in a blundering disorderly fashion. The work is uneven, . . . with passages of gray dullness.—*New York Tribune.*

THE RIVET IN GRANDFATHER'S NECK

(A Comedy of Limitations)

A conventional Southern story. . . . There is no new discernment, no stimulating social criticism. Mr. Cabell may think that he has discovered . . . these things, and recently, but they are no discoveries to the rest of the world. There is no understanding in this book of social currents of the past, much less of the present. The story is . . . almost banal enough to become a best seller.—CLEMENT WOOD, in *The New York Call.*

Certainly the reading public of both North and South cannot forgive Mr. Cabell for writing a story in which not one man or woman is above reproach, not one who is not besmirched by scandal, not one who has any message of hopefulness to teach us how to live nobly.—*Buffalo News,* New York.

The title is not the only queer thing about Mr. Cabell's novel, . . . but the reviewer fails to find it significant. The women are not the kind one likes to read about, and . . . the heroine is a good deal of a fool. The scheme of the book is impossible, and . . . it is a mass of commonplaces, through which is run a thread of the wildly improbable. . . . The book is illogical in the extreme, and . . . it is not one that is likely to be long discussed or remembered.—*Brooklyn Eagle,* New York.

A story of the Robert W. Chambers sort. . . . If the book is typical, there can be no regret that such people are disappearing.—*Springfield Republican,* Massachusetts.

THE CERTAIN HOUR

(*Dizain des Poëtes*)

A collection of "romantic" tales about poets dead and gone, prefaced by a fatuous essay on literature. . . . Two poems, far from poetic, are included in the book.—*The Independent*, New York.

After indulging in a trite and tedious prologue, in which he virtually goes over the ground we covered in college, on the significance of American literature, and gives his reasons for believing there is nothing worth while in literature at this time, the author offers some dozen short stories to prove his point— stories of his own composition. . . . Does not create the proper illusions. . . . The author is not true to the people and the times with which he deals. . . . Readers will prefer Mr. Black's novel "Judith Shakespeare," . . . or, for pure enjoyment, we might prefer "The Jessamy Bride."—*Philadelphia Press*.

The tales might be successful if Mr. Cabell's literary taste were truer—but he is one of the most pretentiously attitudinizing of American authors.—*London Times*, England.

THE CORDS OF VANITY

(A Comedy of Shirking)

About as poor stuff as one can find in a book put out by reputable publishers. . . . The whole thing is slushy and disgusting.—*Cleveland Plain Dealer*, Ohio.

There is very little in the book either in manner or matter to commend it.—*Utica Observer*, New York.

The frontispiece is about the only commendable feature of "The Cords of Vanity."—*New York World*.

Why any author should waste his time in writing the memoirs of a heartless, selfish, penniless and conceited libertine, is more than most readers of this book will be able to understand. . . . Pity it is that some more elevating subject might not be chosen.—*Portland Journal*, Oregon.

We close the book with a disposition to ponder upon the singular perversity of those who need a trespass-warning to keep them from so sterile and malodorous a field. . . . Worse than immoral—dull. . . . The narrative is cheap and sickly . . . the effect is revolting.—*New York Post*.

Inconsequent and rambling, . . rather nauseating at times, ... a series of episodes of cold-blooded sordidness, . . a very unpleasant theme, . . . a most disreputable character for hero. . . . We cannot go further than this in commendation of the book.—A. L. SESSIONS, in *Ainslee's Magazine*.

THE SOUL OF MELICENT

(A Comedy of Woman-Worship)

The book is well bound, with colored illustrations.—*Detroit News-Tribune.*

There are four illustrations in color by Howard Pyle.—*News-Leader*, Richmond, Virginia.

The illustrations by Howard Pyle are gems of his talent as a colorist.—*Philadelphia Press.*

The book is attractively printed, with illustrations by Howard Pyle.—*Boston Globe.*

The story is illustrated with full-page pictures in color by Howard Pyle.—*Pittsburgh Chronicle Telegraph.*

The Pyle pictures are exceedingly spirited and colorful.—*Brooklyn Standard Union*, New York.

Will make a suitable Christmas present to a girl, and is illustrated in color by Howard Pyle.—JOSEPH M. QUENTIN, in *The Portland Oregonian*, Oregon.

CHIVALRY
(Dizain des Reines)

GALLANTRY
(Dizain des Fêtes Galantes)

THE LINE OF LOVE
(Septain des Mariages)

As to "Chivalry," it requires a nicer touch than Mr. Cabell's to reproduce the atmosphere of the Middle Ages; Wardour Street English is not enough. In these stories the artifice is more apparent than the art; it is the sort of playing at antiquity which only genius can make endurable. However, the book contains a number of illustrations in color from paintings mostly by Mr. Pyle. These are admirably done.—*Providence Journal,* Rhode Island.

In "Gallantry" the characters, their costumes, manners, ideas and actions have about the naturalness of a modern costume ball. The author tries hard to maintain a stilted style, but frequently loses patience with it and relieves himself with the most modern of slang. Mr. Howard Pyle outdoes himself in glaring color and meagre composition.—*New York Sun.*

"The Line of Love" is execrable and unforgiveable. . . . It is as though a painter, picturing the fair face and form of some youthful maiden, should with morbid insistence paint in also the lungs that vivify her, the heart that sends her young blood bounding, and the spreading nerves that tingle to her joy. Such love for truth is an unworthy remnant of that dull and ugly realism that at one time threatened to darken all our literature. If Mr. Cabell merely affects it, his fault is unforgivable. If his belief in this phase of art is genuine, then we can but hope for his early enlightenment. . . . But one almost forgets the text, for pleasure in Howard Pyle's odd and deep-hued pictures.—*Leader,* Richmond, Virginia.

THE EAGLE'S SHADOW

(*A Comedy of Purse-Strings*)

Tells a moss-covered story. . . . Such a paleozoic idea demands novelty of treatment. . . . Cabell deals with it in a stodgy way, and tries to freshen it up by some absurd caricatures.—*Cleveland Plain Dealer*, Ohio.

The novel is poorly written, and shows an immaturity of style hardly excusable in print.—*Springfield Republican*, Massachusetts.

The dialogue and bumptious style of the author overshadow the story. . . . The reader is not allowed to devote unqualified attention to anything but the insistent personality of the author. If he is ever distracted therefrom it is only by the inanities and vapid conversations of the dramatis personæ.—*Milwaukee Wisconsin*.

A more painfully jocose book can hardly be imagined. . . . The satire is crude and clumsy. The book is journeyman's work throughout, and it does not deserve the space taken for saying so.—*Providence Journal*, Rhode Island.

A boudoir budget of romantic absurdities. . . . But with time and experience, aided by the sympathetic appreciation of the reviewer, Mr. Cabell will doubtless learn.—*New York Sun*.